SADLIER-OXFORD

Progress in Mathematics
Critical Thinking
For Active Math Minds

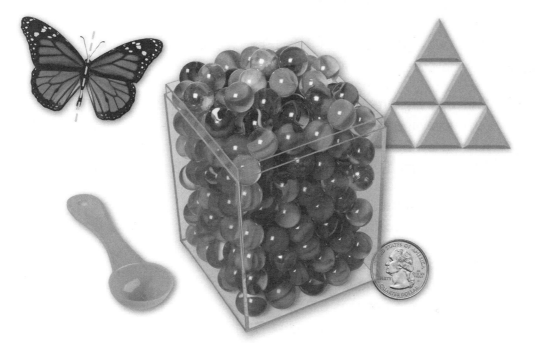

Sadlier-Oxford
A Division of William H. Sadlier, Inc.
www.progressinmathematics.com

Contents

Dear Student

It is sometimes difficult to choose the correct answer to a multiple-choice question test. Often, more than one answer choice can seem to be the right one. *Critical Thinking for Active Math Minds* will help you to make the correct choice.

This booklet will help you use critical thinking strategies. These strategies will help you to decide exactly what a question asks and will help you to analyze each answer choice to select the one that answers the question.

How Can You Build Your Critical Thinking Skills?

There are three different types of lessons in *Critical Thinking for Active Math Minds.* Each of the following lesson types will help you build the critical thinking skills that will lead to success in mathematics.

Chapter-by-Chapter Workshops

- *Critical Thinking for Active Math Minds* has three 2-page workshops for each chapter of *Progress in Mathematics, Grade 4.* The first page has multiple-choice questions and strategies to help you think critically about the answer choices. Look at the parts of a Workshop page below:

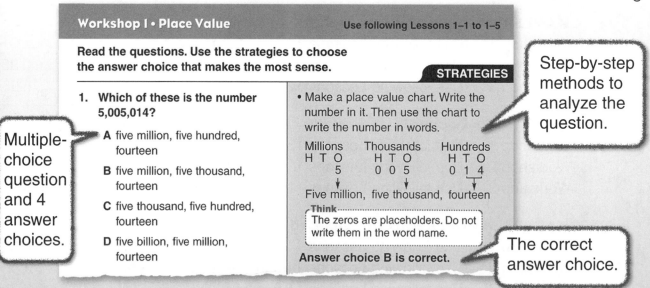

- The second workshop page is your chance to practice your critical-thinking skills. If you get stuck on a question, you can always look back at the first Workshop page, find a similar problem, and review the strategy.

Problem-Solving Workshops

• *Critical Thinking for Active Math Minds* has four 6-page Problem-Solving workshops. These workshops guide you to think critically about each part of a word problem before you try to solve the whole problem.

• Each Problem-Solving Workshop begins with a word problem. The other parts of the Workshop help you to break the problem into smaller parts. Here is an example:

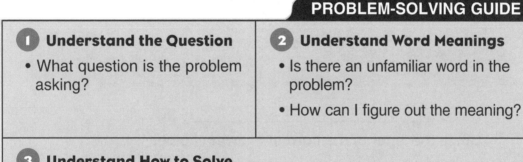

PROBLEM-SOLVING GUIDE

1 Understand the Question
• What question is the problem asking?

2 Understand Word Meanings
• Is there an unfamiliar word in the problem?
• How can I figure out the meaning?

3 Understand How to Solve
• What do I already know?
• How can I use what I know to solve the problem?

4 Circle the Letter of the Correct Answer Choice.
• Reread the problem. Does the answer choice answer the question that the problem is asking?

• The second page of the Problem-Solving Workshop will give you a chance to test your understanding. You will be asked to use what you have learned to analyze and solve a word problem. Remember, you can always look back at the first Workshop page to help you.

• The next four pages of each Problem-Solving Workshop give you many chances to solve word problems on your own. You can use the Critical Thinking Strategies that you learned and practiced in the Problem-Solving Workshops to choose the correct answer to each problem.

Cumulative Reviews: Connecting Concepts

- *Critical Thinking for Active Math Minds* has four reviews that put together the math concepts that you have learned. Each question in these reviews connects a number of mathematical concepts.

- For example, you know addition, multiplication, and division facts. You know how to use the order of operations to compute. You also know how to find part of a set.

- This Cumulative Review question connects all these concepts:

Cumulative Review: Connecting Concepts

Name _____

Circle the letter of the correct answer choice.

1. **Which part of a set completes the number sentence below?**

$$2 + 4 \div 2 \times 3 = \square$$

A $\frac{1}{2}$ of 18   **C** $\frac{1}{4}$ of 32

B $\frac{1}{6}$ of 6   **D** $\frac{1}{2}$ of 6

- To choose the correct answer choice, you need to follow the order of operations. First, work from left to right as you divide and multiply, and then add 2. You need to know the basic facts $4 \div 2 = 2$, $2 \times 3 = 6$, and $2 + 6 = 8$. Finally, you need to divide by a denominator to find part of a number.

- Once you have connected these concepts, you know that your answer choice must equal 8. So the correct answer choice is **C** because $\frac{1}{4}$ of 32 = 8.

We have written these books to provide you with ideas, suggestions, and strategies to help you approach tests with multiple-choice questions with confidence in your ability to apply critical thinking skills to mathematics.

Read the questions. Use the strategies to choose the answer choice that makes the most sense.

STRATEGIES

1. **Which of these is the number 5,005,014?**

   A five million, five hundred, fourteen

   B five million, five thousand, fourteen

   C five thousand, five hundred, fourteen

   D five billion, five million, fourteen

- Make a place value chart. Write the number in it. Then use the chart to write the number in words.

Millions	Thousands	Hundreds
H T O	H T O	H T O
5	0 0 5	0 1 4

Five million, five thousand, fourteen

Think

The zeros are placeholders. Do not write them in the word name.

Answer choice B is correct.

2. **The estimated population of California is 39 million. What is this number in standard form?**

   A 30,900   C 30,900,000

   B 39,000   D 39,000,000

Think

39 million in standard form must begin with 39.

- Which answer choices begin with 39?

   B **39**,000

   D **39**,000,000

Answer choice D is correct. 39 is in the millions place.

3. **Which of these statements about the results of a bean-guessing contest is reported as an estimate?**

   A The winning guess is 2,463 beans.

   B The winner received a $750.00 prize.

   C There were close to 50,000 entries.

   D The greatest guess was 4,789 beans.

Remember
- An estimate is not an exact amount.
- Estimates are rounded numbers.

Analyze each answer choice.

- **A** and **D** are not rounded numbers. They are not estimates.
- **B** looks like a rounded number, but prize amounts are not given as estimates.

Answer choice C is correct. The words *close to* are a clue that the amount is not exact, so 50,000 is an estimate.

Circle the letter of the correct answer choice.

4. Which is 5000 less than three hundred five million, sixty thousand?

A 300,060,000   C 305,055,000

B 305,059,500   D 305,065,000

5. Which is the word name for the number in the place value chart?

MILLIONS PERIOD			THOUSANDS PERIOD			ONES PERIOD		
HUNDREDS	TENS	ONES	HUNDREDS	TENS	ONES	HUNDREDS	TENS	ONES
3	0	6	7	0	0	0	3	0

A thirty-six million, seven thousand, thirty

B three-hundred million, seven hundred thousand

C three hundred six million, seven hundred thousand, thirty

D three million, sixty-seven thousand, thirty

6. What is 14 million, 9 hundred thousand in standard form?

A 1,400,900   C 14,009,000

B 14,000,900   D 14,900,000

7. Which is 100 more than 13,487?

A 14,487   C 134,287

B 13,587   D 133,587

8. Which of these is the word name for the number 21,001,460?

A twenty-one million, ten thousand, four hundred sixty

B twenty-one million, one thousand, four hundred sixty

C twenty million, one hundred ten thousand, four hundred six

D twenty-one million, one hundred thousand, four hundred sixty

9. Which is standard form for sixty-four thousand, eighty-one?

A 64,081   C 64,810

B 600,481   D 640,081

10. Which statement about Yellowstone National Park is an estimate?

A In 2006, Yellowstone had over 2,800,000 visitors.

B In 1896, Yellowstone had 4,659 visitors.

C Yellowstone consists of 2,221,766 acres.

D A yearly visitor's permit to Yellowstone costs $40.00.

Read the questions. Use the strategies to choose
the answer choice that makes the most sense.

STRATEGIES

1. **Which of these numbers has the greatest value?**

   A 22,526

   B 22,653

   C 22,156

   D 21,965

- Write the numbers in expanded form.
- Compare each place value.

   A 20,000 + 2000 + 500 + 20 + 6

   B 20,000 + 2000 + 600 + 50 + 3

   C 20,000 + 2000 + 100 + 50 + 6

   D 20,000 + 1000 + 900 + 60 + 5

Ten-thousands: 20,000 = 20,000
Thousands: 1000 < 2000.
Choice D, 21,965, is not correct.

Hundreds: 600 > 500 > 100
$\quad$ **22,6**53 > **22,5**20 > **22,1**50 > 21,965

Answer choice B, 22,653, is correct.

---

2. **Which money amount has the greatest value?**

   A $1.88

   B $1.03

   C $1.89

   D $1.00

- Line up the amounts. Compare their values.

	Dollars	Dimes	Pennies
A	1	8	8
B	1	0	3
C	1	8	9
D	1	0	0

Think
0 has no value.

Dollars: 1 = 1 **Dimes:** 8 = 8 **Pennies:** 9 > 8 > 3
$\quad$ $1.89 > $1.88 > $1.03 > $1.00

Choice C, $1.89, is correct.

---

3. **Which letter is above the point that is at about 641 on the number line?**

   A P   **C** R

   B Q   **D** S

Think
641 must be between 640 and 660.

- Points *Q* and *R* are between 640 and 660.
- Point *R* is halfway between 640 and 660.
- Point *Q* is closer to 640 than Point *R*.

Answer Choice B, Point Q, is correct.

Name _____

Circle the letter of the correct answer choice.

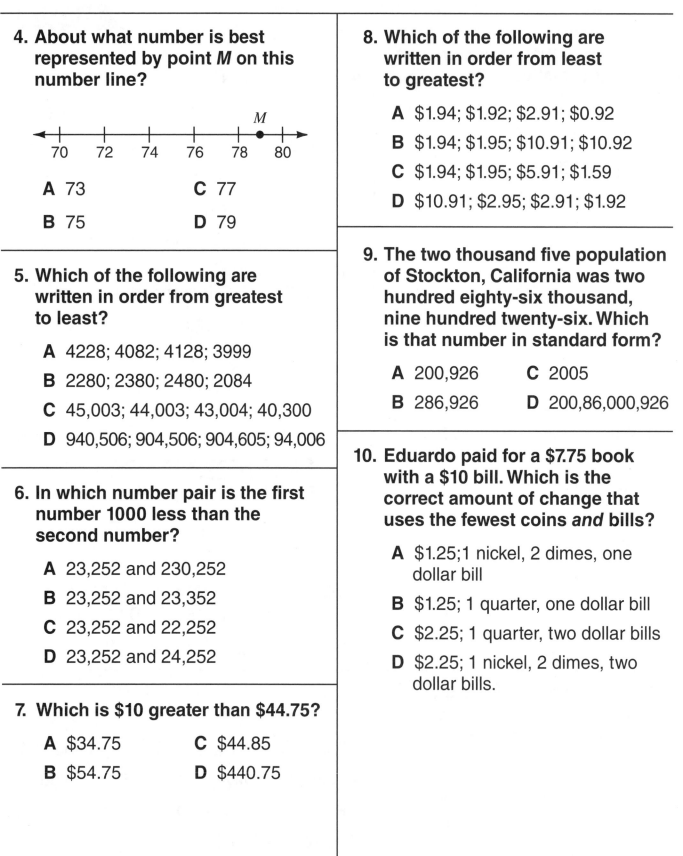

4. **About what number is best represented by point *M* on this number line?**

A 73   C 77

B 75   D 79

5. **Which of the following are written in order from greatest to least?**

A 4228; 4082; 4128; 3999

B 2280; 2380; 2480; 2084

C 45,003; 44,003; 43,004; 40,300

D 940,506; 904,506; 904,605; 94,006

6. **In which number pair is the first number 1000 less than the second number?**

A 23,252 and 230,252

B 23,252 and 23,352

C 23,252 and 22,252

D 23,252 and 24,252

7. **Which is $10 greater than $44.75?**

A $34.75   C $44.85

B $54.75   D $440.75

8. **Which of the following are written in order from least to greatest?**

A $1.94; $1.92; $2.91; $0.92

B $1.94; $1.95; $10.91; $10.92

C $1.94; $1.95; $5.91; $1.59

D $10.91; $2.95; $2.91; $1.92

9. **The two thousand five population of Stockton, California was two hundred eighty-six thousand, nine hundred twenty-six. Which is that number in standard form?**

A 200,926   C 2005

B 286,926   D 200,86,000,926

10. **Eduardo paid for a $7.75 book with a $10 bill. Which is the correct amount of change that uses the fewest coins *and* bills?**

A $1.25;1 nickel, 2 dimes, one dollar bill

B $1.25; 1 quarter, one dollar bill

C $2.25; 1 quarter, two dollar bills

D $2.25; 1 nickel, 2 dimes, two dollar bills.

Read the questions. Use the strategies to choose the answer choice that makes the most sense.

1. **What is 46,738 rounded to the nearest thousand?**

   A 40,000

   B 47,000

   C 46,600

   D 46,000

Think
What digit is in the thousands place?

Thousands			Hundreds		
H	T	O	H	T	O
	4	6	7	3	8

- The digit **6** is in the thousands place. Its value is 6000.

- Look at the digit to the right of the thousands place. Its value is 700.

   46,⎡7⎤38

   700 > 500.

- Round 6000 UP to the next thousand.

   6000 rounds to 7000

**Answer choice B is correct.
46,738 rounds to 47,000.**

2. **Jo has 12 roses to put in a vase. She has red roses and yellow roses. For every red rose, Jo has 2 yellow roses. How many yellow roses does Jo have?**

   A 14   **C** 2

   B 24   **D** 8

- Make a table to help you find the correct answer choice.

Think
The table needs a row for red roses, a row for yellow roses, and a row for the total number of roses.

Red	1	2	3	4
Yellow	2	4	6	8
Total	3	6	9	(12)

2 yellow for every 1 red

Add each column. Stop when you have 12 roses.

4 red roses and **8 yellow roses** equal **12 roses** in all.

**Answer choice D is correct.
Jo has 8 yellow roses.**

Circle the letter of the correct answer choice.

3. Ben has $20 to spend on school supplies. He buys 3 of the items on this price list.

Supplies	Price
Notebook	$3.89
Pen	$2.79
Calculator	$13.40
Backpack	$14.98

Use rounding to decide which item Ben *did not* buy.

A calculator   C pen

B notebook   D backpack

4. In 2005, the population of San Jose, California was 912,332. What is 912,332 rounded to the nearest ten thousand?

A 900,00   C 912,000

B 910,000   D 913,000

5. Which number belongs in the box to show the numbers in order from the greatest to the least?

67,003   63,588   [   ]   61,204

A 60,997   C 64,826

B 68,921   D 63,007

6. Ruth has 6 blue beads. She has 3 yellow beads for every blue bead. Which table shows how many yellow beads Ruth has *and* how many beads she has in all?

Color	Number of Beads					
Blue	1	2	3	4	5	6
Yellow	3	3	3	3	3	3
Total	4	5	6	7	8	9

A

Color	Number of Beads					
Blue	1	2	3	4	5	6
Yellow	3	6	9	12	15	18
Total	4	8	12	16	20	24

B

Color	Number of Beads					
Blue	1	2	3	4	5	6
Yellow	3	5	6	7	8	9
Total	4	7	9	11	13	15

C

Color	Number of Beads					
Blue	1	2	3	4	5	6
Yellow	1	2	3	4	5	6
Total	2	4	6	8	10	12

D

Read the questions. Use the strategies to choose the answer choice that makes the most sense.

STRATEGIES

1. Li rode her bicycle 5 miles on Monday, 4 miles on Tuesday, and 2 miles on Wednesday. She rode the same number of miles on Thursday as she did on Monday. How many miles did she ride in all?

   A 5425   **C** 12

   B 16   **D** 11

   Think
   Li rode 5 miles on both Monday and Thursday. Add 5 + 4 + 2 + 5 to find the total.

   You can add the four addends in any order.

   - Look for sums of 10.
     Change the order and the grouping.
     $$5 + 5 + 4 + 2$$
     $$10 + 4 + 2$$

   - Add the other two addends to 10.
     $$10 + 4 + 2 = 16$$

   Answer choice B is correct.
   $$5 + 4 + 2 + 5 = 16$$

2. What is the value of *n*?

   $$16 - n = 9$$

   A 25   **C** 9

   B 17   **D** 7

   Think
   16 minus a number equals 9. Find the missing subtrahend.

   $$16 - n = 9$$
   - Use a related addition fact.
     $9 + n = 16$, so $9 + 7 = 16$

   Remember: Addition undoes subtraction.

   - Use a related subtraction fact.
     $16 - 9 = n$, so $16 - 9 = 7$

   Answer choice D, 7, is correct.

3. There are 20 cars in the parking lot. Some of them are red. Which expression shows how many cars in the lot are not red?

   A $10 + 10$ **C** $20 - r$

   B $r - 20$ **D** $20 + r$

   The number of red cars is an *unknown part* of the *whole* set of 20 cars. You can subtract to show the *part* that is not red.

   total number of cars − unknown number of red cars

   $20 - r$ ← A variable stands for an unknown number.

   Answer choice C, $20 - r$, is correct.

Circle the letter of the correct answer choice.

---

4. **Which of the following is true?**

   A $5 + 8 = 8 + 5$

   B $4 + 0 = 0$

   C $(3 + 7) + 4 = 3 + (7 + 3)$

   D $9 + 4 = 9 - 4$

---

5. **Jerome is on vacation. He mails 2 postcards on the first day, 5 on the second day, 8 on the third day, and 3 on the fourth day. How many postcards does he mail in all?**

   A 4   **C** 18

   B 16   **D** 20

---

6. **Dan has 4 baseball caps. Sari has 7 baseball caps. How many more caps does Sari have than Dan?**

   A 3   **C** 7

   B 4   **D** 11

---

7. **Which number sentence would best help find the missing addend?**

   $$n + 7 = 11$$

   A $11 - 7 = 4$ **C** $1 + 7 = 8$

   B $7 - 1 = 6$ **D** $7 + 11 = 18$

---

8. **Tran swims some laps in the pool. Mei swims 2 more laps than Tran. Which expression shows how many laps Mei swims?**

   A $s - 2$ **C** $2 - s$

   B $s + s$ **D** $s + 2$

---

9. **Which problem matches the following expression?**

   $$12 - c$$

   A Alex eats 12 carrot sticks. How many does Anna eat?

   B Alex eats 12 carrot sticks. What is the difference between the number he eats and the number Anna eats?

   C Anna eats 12 more carrot sticks than Alex. How many does Alex eat?

   D Alex eats 12 carrot sticks. Anna eats c more carrot sticks than Alex. How many does she eat?

---

10. **What is the value of the expression $b + 7$, when $b = 8$?**

    A 1   **C** 15

    B $7 + b$ **D** $b + 15$

Read the questions. Use the strategies to choose the answer choice that makes the most sense.

STRATEGIES

1. Jenn counts 28 large signs and 43 small signs while she rides in the car. She adds mentally to find the total number of signs. How many signs does Jenn see?

   A 75   **C** 70

   B 71   **D** 55

Add 28 + 43 mentally.

• Use *compensation*. Balance what you do to one addend by doing the opposite to the other addend.

Think
28 is close to 30. You can make a ten.

$$\begin{array}{r} 28 + \mathbf{2} \rightarrow \ \ \ 30 \\ + 43 - \mathbf{2} \rightarrow + 41 \\ \hline 71 \end{array}$$

Add 2 to 28 to make 30.
Subtract 2 from 43.

• *Break apart numbers*.

$$28 + 43 = n$$
$$(20 + 8) + (40 + 3)$$
$$(20 + 40) + (8 + 3)$$
$$60 + 11 = 71$$

Add the tens.
Add the ones.

Answer choice B, 71, is correct.

2. Tony buys a hat and a jacket. He spends $26.98. The hat costs $4.23. How much does the jacket cost?

   A $22.00

   B $22.75

   C $22.98

   D $26.98

Think
Subtract the cost of the hat from $26.98.

$$\$26.98 - \$4.23 = \square$$

• Estimate. Round to the nearest dollar.
Round up $26.**98** to $27.00. ← 9 > 5
Round down $4.**23** to $4.00. ← 2 < 5
$27.00 − $4.00 = $23.00

• Subtract.

$$\begin{array}{r} \$26.98 \\ - \ \ 4.23 \\ \hline \$22.75 \end{array}$$

Subtracting money is like subtracting whole numbers. Write the $ and . in the answer.

$22.75 is close to $23.00
The answer is reasonable.

Answer choice B is correct.

Circle the letter of the correct answer choice.

3. Liam likes to add mentally. Which best shows how he could add 51 + 36 mentally?

   A 5 tens + 4 tens

   B (50 + 30) + (10 + 40)

   C (51 − 1) + (36 + 1)

   D (5 + 3) + (1 + 6)

4. Which of the following is a reasonable estimated sum or difference?

   A $58 - 17 = n$; about 30

   B $71 + 20 = n$; about 100

   C $21{,}714 + 115 = n$; about 21,800

   D $75{,}589 - 2{,}467 = n$; about 70,100

5. Michael always estimates before he subtracts. Which best shows how he rounds to estimate the difference for the following?

$$3827 - 491$$

   A 3800 − 500

   C 4000 − 1000

   B 3840 − 490

   D 3800 − 400

6. On Monday, Mia collects $41.20. On Tuesday, she collects $57.75. How much money does she collect in all?

   A $16.55

   B $57.75

   C $61.87

   D $98.95

7. Which is the most reasonable estimate of the following sum?

$$6859$$
$$523$$
$$+ \ 2324$$

   A About 8500

   B About 9700

   C About 10,000

   D About 14,000

8. Mr. Ito had $57.60. He bought stamps for $47.15. How much money did he have left?

   A $11.45

   B $11.00

   C $10.45

   D $10.00

Read the questions. Use the strategies to choose the answer choice that makes the most sense.

1. Elena buys a skateboard for $52.20 and a helmet for $44.19. How much does she spend in all?

   A $8.01

   B $90.00

   C $96.01

   D $96.39

Remember: Adding dollars and cents is like adding whole numbers.

- **Add.** Write the dollar sign and the decimal point in the sum.

$$\begin{array}{r} \$52.20 \\ +\ 44.19 \\ \hline \$96.39 \end{array}$$

- **Check the answer.**

Think
Subtraction undoes addition.

$$\begin{array}{r} \$96.39 \\ -\ 44.19 \\ \hline \$52.20 \end{array} \quad \begin{array}{r} \$96.39 \\ -\ 52.20 \\ \hline \$44.19 \end{array}$$

Start with the sum. Subtract one addend. The difference is the other addend.

So the addition is correct.

Answer choice D, $96.39, is correct.

2. Tom uses 576 beads to make a wall hanging. Lauren uses 213 beads to make a necklace. How many more beads does Tom use?

   A 213

   B 363

   C 400

   D 789

Think
The words *how many more* are a clue that you must *subtract* to find the difference between the greater and lesser amounts.

- **Subtract.**

$$\begin{array}{r} 576 \\ -\ 213 \\ \hline 363 \end{array}$$

Think
Addition undoes subtraction.

- **Check the answer.**

$$\begin{array}{r} 576 \\ -\ 213 \\ \hline 363 \end{array} \quad \begin{array}{r} 363 \\ +\ 213 \\ \hline 576 \end{array}$$

Start with the difference. Add the number subtracted.

These numbers are the same.

So the subtraction is correct.

Answer choice B, 363, is correct.

Name _____

Circle the letter of the correct answer choice.

3. Justin added two numbers. Which of the following shows how he checks the sum?

$$540 \atop + \ 223$$

A $540 \atop - \ 223$ C $763 \atop - \ 223$

B $540 \atop + \ 223$ D $700 \atop - \ 200$

4. Kate sees 3 cats on Monday and double that number on Tuesday. On Wednesday she sees 2 more than on Tuesday. How many cats does she see altogether?

A 17   C 11

B 13   D 7

5. In April scientists find 122 tools at a digging site. In May they find more tools and now have a total of 456 tools. Approximately how many tools do they find in May?

A 300   C 580

B 400   D 600

6. What is the value of the expression $y - 4$, when $y = 12$?

A 16   C 4

B 8   D 3

7. Cody buys four gifts for $20.95, $3.98, $12.25, and $31.90. Which of the following shows about how much he spends when each price is rounded to the nearest dollar?

A $60.00

B $66.00

C $69.00

D $70.00

8. Niki makes some paper swans. Phil makes 4 more swans than Niki. Which expression shows how many swans Phil makes?

A 4

B $s - 4$

C $4 - s$

D $s + 4$

9. Avi buys a baseball glove for $64.49 and a bat for $33.10. He subtracts to find that the baseball glove costs $31.39 more than the bat. He adds to check whether he is correct. Which two amounts does he add?

A $31.39 + $33.10

B $31.39 + $64.49

C $64.49 + $33.10

D $30.00 + $30.00

Read the questions. Use the strategies to choose the answer choice that makes the most sense.

1. The table shows the number of students in the Apple Valley schools. About how many students are in the schools altogether?

Apple Valley Schools	
School	**Number of Students**
East Side	1450
South Side	2650
West Side	1980

A about 4000

B about 5000

C about 6000

D about 7000

- Use front-end estimation.
- Add front digits.

Think
About means to estimate.

$$
\begin{array}{r}
1450 \\
2650 \\
+\ 1980 \\
\hline
4000
\end{array}
$$
⬆⬆⬆ Write zeros.

- Make groups of about 1000 to adjust the estimate.

1450 ⎫
2650 ⎬ about 1000
+ 1980 — about 1000
6000 **Adjusted estimate**

- Use rounding.

1450 + 2650 + 1980   Round to the
  ↓   ↓   ↓   nearest thousand.
1000 + 3000 + 2000 = 6000

Answer choice C, about 6000, is correct.

2. **What is the sum of 2475 and 3816?**

A 6391

B 6291

C 6281

D 5281

Make a place-value chart to thousands.

	th	h	t	o
	1		1	
	2	4	7	5
+	3	8	1	6
	6	2	9	1

Remember: Regroup when there are more than 9 in any place.

Add ones. 5 + 6 = 11 ones
11 > 9; **regroup** as 1 ten 1 one
Add tens. 1 + 7 + 1 = 9 tens
9 = 9; **do not regroup**
Add hundreds. 4 + 8 = 12 hundreds
12 > 9; **regroup** as 1 thousand
2 hundreds
Add thousands. 1 + 2 + 3 = 6 thousands
7 < 9; **do not regroup**

Answer choice B, 6291, is correct.

Name _____

Circle the letter of the correct answer choice.

3. Mr. Bruno drove his truck 457 miles one week, 712 miles the next week, and 644 miles the third week. About how many miles did he drive in the three weeks?

   A about 600 miles

   B about 1700 miles

   C about 1800 miles

   D about 2000 miles

4.
$$\begin{array}{r} 681 \\ + 258 \\ \hline \end{array}$$

   A 1000

   B 939

   C 839

   D 423

5. Each student at Central College voted one time for most valuable player. Willa received 2634 votes. Jose received 3927 votes, and Lonnie received 1892 votes. How many students voted?

   A 8453

   B 8443

   C 8353

   D 7453

6. During Week One 2,057,094 people visited the state web site. During Week Two 888,706 people visited the site. How many people visited the web site during those two weeks?

   A 2,835,790

   B 2,935,790

   C 2,945,790

   D 2,945,800

7. $7.08 + $43.56 = □

   A $50.54

   B $50.64

   C $51.64

   D $114.36

8. Luis spent $44.75, $52.98, and $38.75 on groceries. How much did he spend on groceries altogether?

   A $97.73

   B $135.48

   C $136.48

   D $146.48

Read the questions. Use the strategies to choose the answer choice that makes the most sense.

1. **Jack needs 6000 points to win a game. He already has 4275 points. How many more points does he need to win?**

   A 1725

   B 1825

   C 2000

   D 2725

Subtract to find how many more points Jack needs.

$$6000 - 4275 = \square$$

Look at the zeros in the minuend.

Think
You cannot subtract a number greater than zero from zero. More hundreds, tens, and ones are needed.

- Write the subtraction in a place value chart.
- Regroup *all*.
- Then subtract.

th	h	t	o
	9	9	
5	10	10	10
6	0	0	0
−4	2	7	5

th	h	t	o
	9	9	
5	10	10	10
6	0	0	0
−4	2	7	5
1	7	2	5

Think
6 thousands = 5 thousands 10 hundreds
10 hundreds = 9 hundreds 10 tens
10 tens = 9 tens 10 ones

- Check.

Estimate	Add
6000	1725
− 4000	+ 4275
2000	6000

Answer choice A, 1725, is correct.

Circle the letter of the correct answer choice.

2. The Oroville Dam is 770 feet high. The Hungry Horse Dam is 564 feet high. How much higher than the Hungry Horse Dam is the Oroville Dam?

 A 1334 feet

 B 216 feet

 C 206 feet

 D 106 feet

3. $2196.04 − $682.29 = ☐

 A $1513.85

 B $1513.75

 C $1512.75

 D $1502.75

4. Lisa gives nature talks at the zoo. In May, 244 people came to hear Lisa. She spoke to 189 people in June. How many more people heard Lisa's talk in May than in June?

 A 55

 B 158

 C 168

 D 244

5. Sid buys a case of blank CDs for $22.95. He gives the cashier $30.00. How much change does he get?

 A $2.05

 B $2.95

 C $7.05

 D $8.05

6.   7000
   − 277

 A 423

 B 6723

 C 6823

 D 7277

7. The Milton family drives through two tunnels. One tunnel is 5808 feet long. The other tunnel is 1575 feet shorter. How long is the other tunnel?

 A 1575 feet

 B 4223 feet

 C 4233 miles

 D 4233 feet

Workshop 3 • Addition and Subtraction Use following Lessons 3-10 to 3-12.

Read the questions. Use the strategies to choose
the answer choice that makes the most sense.

STRATEGIES

1. 42,165 + 3082 + 96,841 = ☐

  A 131,988

  B 142,000

  C 142,088

  D 169,826

• First, use rounding to estimate the sum.

Think
Round each number to the greatest place of
the least number.

$$42,000 + 3,000 + 97,000 = 142,000$$

• Align the addends by place value.
Start by adding the ones.

```
  1 1 1
  42,165
   3,082
+ 96,841
 142,088
```

Remember: Regroup
when there are more
than 9 in any place.

The sum 142,088 is close to the estimate of
142,000. The answer is reasonable.

Answer choice C, 142,088, is correct.

2. $700.00 − $26.59 = ☐

  A $670.00

  B $673.41

  C $684.51

  D $726.59

• First, use rounding to estimate.
$700.00 − $30.00 = $670.00

• Align the numbers by place value.

Think
There are zeros in the minuend. You must
regroup before starting to subtract.

• Regroup as many   • Subtract.
times as needed.

```
    9  9  9                    9  9  9
  6 10 10 10 10             6 10 10 10 10
 $7  0  0. 0  0            $7  0  0. 0  0
 −     2  6. 5  9          −     2  6. 5  9
                           $6  7  3. 4  1
```

$673.41 is close to the estimate of $670.00.
The answer is reasonable.

Answer choice B, $673.41, is correct.

Copyright © by William H. Sadlier, Inc. All rights reserved.

Name _____

Circle the letter of the correct answer choice.

3. John is an actor in a play. During the first week, 3835 people saw the play. During the second week, 477 fewer people saw the play. How many people saw the play during the second week?

   A 477   **C** 3442

   B 3358   **D** 4312

4. A diver searches for golf balls that landed in a pond. He finds 156 golf balls the first day, 231 golf balls the second day, and 107 golf balls the third day. About how many golf balls does he find in all?

   A about 200

   B about 300

   C about 400

   D about 500

5. $50.00
   −   28.46

   A $1.29   **C** $21.54

   B $4.76   **D** $26.24

6. Inez spent $15.75 on gloves, $30.99 on a scarf, and $18 on a hat. How much did she spend in all?

   A $64.74   **C** $46.92

   B $53.64   **D** $46.74

7. The span of a bridge in Italy is 10,827 feet long. The span of a bridge in Japan is 6532 feet long. How much longer than the span of the bridge in Japan is the span of the bridge in Italy?

   A 17,359 feet

   B 6532 feet

   C 4295 feet

   D 3285 feet

8. The numbers below increase by the same amount each time. If that continues, what are the next two numbers?

   137, 181, 225, 269, ___, ___

   A 303, 337   **C** 137, 181

   B 313, 357   **D** 44, 44

Read the questions. Use the strategies to choose the answer choice that makes the most sense.

STRATEGIES

1. Which multiplication property does the following demonstrate?

   $(3 \times 3) \times 2 = 3 \times (3 \times 2)$

   A zero property

   B identity property

   C commutative property

   D associative property

Properties can help you multiply.

- **Zero property**
  $0 \times 2 = 0$ and $2 \times 0 = 0$

  Think zero product

- **Identity property**
  $1 \times 2 = 2$ and $2 \times 1 = 2$

  Think same number

- **Commutative property**
  $3 \times 5 = 15$ and $5 \times 3 = 15$

  Think order

- **Associative property**
  $(3 \times 3) \times 2 = 18$ and $3 \times (3 \times 2) = 18$
  $9 \quad \times 2 = 18$ and $3 \times \quad 6 \quad = 18$

  Think grouping

Answer choice D is correct.

2. The parking lot at City Hall has 6 rows. Thirty-two cars can park in each row. How many cars can park in the lot?

   A 242

   B 192

   C 182

   D 38

Think
The same number of cars can park in each row. Multiply 6×32.

- Use front-end digits.
  Estimate. $6 \times 30 = 180$

- Use the distributive property.

  $6 \times 32 = 6 \times (30 + 2)$
  $= (6 \times 30) + (6 \times 2)$
  $= 180 + 12 = 192$

Remember: You can multiply the same factor across two addends.

- Write 6×32 vertically and multiply.
  Multiply the ones.
  6×2 ones $= 12$ ones
  Regroup as **1** ten **2** ones.

tens	ones
1	
3	**2**
$\times$	**6**
	2

  Multiply the tens.
  6×3 tens $= 18$ tens
  18 tens $+ 1$ ten $= 19$ tens

tens	ones
1	
3	2
$\times$	**6**
19	2

- 192 is close to 180.
  The answer is reasonable.

Answer choice B, 192, is correct.

Circle the letter of the correct answer choice.

3. Multiply.

$$(2 \times 3) \times 5 = 2 \times (\square \times 5)$$

   Which number will make the multiplication sentence true?

   A 1

   B 2

   C 3

   D 5

4. Mr. Grace bought 88 pencils of the same color.

Color	Pencils in 1 box
Blue	20
Green	22
Red	24
Yellow	30

   Use the list above. Which color pencil did Mr. Grace buy?

   A blue   **C** red

   B green   **D** yellow

5. Multiply.

   $$\begin{array}{r} 37 \\ \times\ 7 \\ \hline \end{array}$$

   A 217   **C** 259

   B 219   **D** 2149

6. Erin buys 5 boxes of greeting cards. Each box contains 21 cards. About how many greeting cards does Erin buy? Use front-end estimation.

   A about 30

   B about 40

   C about 50

   D about 100

7. Which shows using the distributive property to find 5×23?

   A $(3 \times 20) + (3 \times 5)$

   B $(5 \times 20) + (5 \times 3)$

   C $(5 \times 20) \times (5 \times 3)$

   D $(5 + 20) + (5 + 3)$

8. Look at the riddle below.

   > I have a product of 90.
   > I have two factors.
   > What are my two factors?

   Which answer solves the riddle?

   A 2 and 9

   B 2 and 40

   C 6 and 15

   D 9 and 15

Read the questions. Use the strategies to choose the answer choice that makes the most sense.

1. **Will buys 6 tickets for the concert. Each ticket costs $21.75. How much do the tickets cost in all?**

   A $120.20

   B $126.50

   C $130.50

   D $362.00

Think

Each ticket costs $21.75. Multiply 6 × $21.75.

- Estimate. Use front-end digits.

   $6 \times \$20.00 = \$120.00$ ◄——— $21.75 > $20.00, so the answer is greater than $120.00.

- Multiply money the same way you multiply whole numbers.

$$
\begin{array}{r}
1\ 4\ 3 \\
\$21.75 \\
\times\qquad 6 \\
\hline
\$130.50
\end{array}
$$
◄—Write $ and . in the product.

   > Remember: Add the regrouped amount after you multiply.

- $130.50 is close to $120.00. The answer is reasonable.

Answer choice C, $130.50, is correct.

---

2. **The stadium has 23 seating sections. Each section has 21 seats. How many people are in the stadium if every seat is filled?**

   A 69

   B 400

   C 483

   D 690

Think

You can multiply to find the total of 23 groups of 21.

- First, use rounding to find about what the answer will be.

$$
\begin{array}{r}
21 \longrightarrow 20 \\
\times 23 \longrightarrow \times 20 \\
\hline
\text{about } 400
\end{array}
$$

   > Hint: $2 \times 20 = 40$
   > $20 \times 20 = 400$

- Multiply 23 × 21.

   Multiply by the ones.   Multiply by the tens.
   $3 \times 21 = 63$ $20 \times 21 = 420$

tens	ones
2	1
× 2	3
6	3

Add the partial products.
$63 + 420 = 483$

tens	ones
2	1
× 2	3
6	3
4 2	0
4 8	3

- 483 is close to 400. The answer is reasonable.

Answer choice C, 483, is correct.

Name _____

Circle the letter of the correct answer choice.

3. **Multiply.**

$$4 \times 201 = \square$$

   A 804   C 914

   B 844   D 8004

4. **Greeting cards cost $2.95 each. Kim buys 8 cards. How much does she spend in all?**

   A $16.20

   B $16.60

   C $23.60

   D $29.50

5. **There are 9 classrooms in Sam's school. Each has 1244 square feet of floor space. How much floor space is there altogether in the classrooms?**

   A 11,196 square feet

   B 11,186 square feet

   C 10,196 square feet

   D 1253 square feet

6. **Multiply.**

$$\begin{array}{r} 32 \\ \times\ 24 \\ \hline \end{array}$$

   A 192   C 878

   B 768   D 64,128

7. **Which is true about the product of 30 × 80?**

   A It is less than 200.

   B It is less than the product of 80 × 30.

   C It has 1 zero.

   D It has 2 zeros.

8. **There are 34 boxes of markers in the art supply room. Each box has 480 markers. About how many markers are there?**
   HINT: Estimate to find about how many.

   A about 1500

   B about 15,000

   C about 20,000

   D about 50,000

9. **Nat sold 33 cookies at a bake sale. He charged $.12 for each cookie. How much money did Nat earn?**

   A $.99

   B $3.30

   C $3.96

   D $5.06

Read the questions. Use the strategies to choose the answer choice that makes the most sense.

1. The Art Museum has 74 volunteers. Each volunteer made 525 phone calls to tell members about a new exhibit. How many calls did the volunteers make in all?

   A 5775

   B 38,850

   C 40,050

   D 59,010

Think

You can multiply to find the total of 74 groups of 525. 74×525

- First estimate the product.
  $70 \times 500 = 35,000$ ← 74×525 is about 35,000.

- Multiply 74×525. Use a place-value chart.
- Multiply by the ones.   **4×525**

th	h	t	o
	1	2	
	5	2	5
×		7	4
2	1	0	0

4×525

4×5 ones = 20 ones
  = **2** tens **0** ones
4×2 tens = 8 tens + 2 tens
  = **1** hundred
  0 tens
4×5 hundreds = 20 hundreds
  + 1 hundred
  = **2** thousands
  1 hundred

- Next multiply by the tens.   **70×525**

Remember: Regroup when needed. Add the regrouped amount after you multiply.

th	h	t	o
	1	3	
	1̶	2̶	
	5	2	5
×		7	4
2	1	0	0
36	7	5	0
38,	8	5	0

← Do not add the regrouping for multiplying by the ones.

} Add the partial products.
$2100 + 36,750 = 38,850$

70×525

- 38,850 is close to 35,000.

Answer choice B is correct. 38,850

Circle the letter of the correct answer choice.

2. Mr. Kline mails 18 packages. The postage for each package is $2.89. Which would be the best estimate of the total postage?

   A about $30.00

   B about $40.00

   C about $60.00

   D about $100.00

3. How many zeros will be in the product of 20×800?

   A 1   C 3

   B 2   D 4

4. Lucy orders carpet for 65 apartments. Each apartment has 944 square feet of floor space. How many square feet of carpet does Lucy order?

   A 61,360

   B 56,000

   C 10,384

   D 1009

5. Find the product.

   $$36 \times 18$$

   A 54   C 572

   B 288   D 648

6. Which is true about the product of 70×110?

   A $70 \times 110 < 7000$

   B $70 \times 110 > 14{,}000$

   C $70 \times 110 < 110 \times 70$

   D 70×110 is about 7000

7. Ace Foods delivers 75 cases of juice to the food bank. There are 44 cans in each case. How many cans of juice does Ace Foods deliver to the food bank?

   A 3500

   B 3300

   C 3200

   D 119

8. It costs $6.36 to buy a science kit. If each of the 29 students in Logan's class buys a kit, what is the total cost for the kits?

   A $184.44   C $69.96

   B $181.44   D $57.24

9. Multiply.

   $$42 \times 240$$

   A 1440   C 10,080

   B 5280   D 10,122

Read the problem. Use the Problem-Solving Guide below to help you think about the answer choices.

Lou and two friends went to lunch at a restaurant. When the bill came, Lou's portion of the cost was $8.20. Lou paid with a $20 bill. How much money did he receive as change?

A $12.80   C $11.80

B $12.50   D $11.70

PROBLEM-SOLVING GUIDE

1 Understand the Question

- The question is asking you to find the answer choice that shows how much money Lou had left after buying his lunch.
- Each answer choice shows a different amount of money.

2 Understand Word Meanings

- *bill* and *portion* are multiple-meaning words. *Bill* can mean "request for payment" or "paper money." *Portion* can mean "a part of something" or "a helping of food."
- You can decide on the meaning by the way the word is used in a sentence.
- In this problem, *portion* means "part." *Bill* is used two ways. Lou has to pay his part of the *bill* which he pays with paper money.

3 Understand How to Solve

- Reread the question if you need to.
- Choose the operation to solve the problem.
- Subtract $20 – $8.20 to find the difference.

$$\$20.00 - \$8.20 = \$11.80$$

- Find the answer choice that is $11.80.

.Think
You need to find the **difference** between two money amounts.

4 Circle the Letter of the Correct Answer Choice.

Answer choice C is correct. Lou received $11.80 in change.

Name _____

Circle the letter of the correct answer choice.

The table shows attendance at a 3-day crafts fair.

About how many people in all attended the crafts fair on the three days? Use front-end estimation.

Craft Fair Attendance	
Day	People
1	2754
2	2197
3	3875

A 7000   **C** 9000

B 8000   **D** 10,000

Complete each sentence.

1 Understand the Question

• The table shows the number of _____ who attended the _____.

• The question is asking you to find _____.

---

2 Understand Word Meanings: attended

• Your teacher takes *attendance* in school. *Attended* and *attendance* both contain the word "attend."

• **Attended** is another word for _____.

---

3 Understand How to Solve

• Add the front digits. _____ + _____ + _____ = _____

• Write zeros for the other digits to get a rough estimate.

_____ + _____ + _____ is about _____

• Make groups of 1000 from the other digits: 2754 + 2197   +   3875

                            about 1000   + about 1000

• The adjusted estimate is about _____ + _____ + _____ + _____ + _____ = _____

---

4 Circle the Letter of the Correct Answer Choice.

Answer choice _____ is correct. _____ is a reasonable estimate.

Circle the letter of the correct answer choice.

1. The table shows the highest points in five states.

   Use the table to answer the question below.

State and Mountain	Altitude (ft)
Alabama; Cheaha Mt.	2407
Arizona; Humphreys Peak	12,633
Maine; Mt. Katahdin	5268
Colorado; Mt. Elbert	14,433
Vermont; Mt. Mansfield	4393

   Which mountain is higher than Mt. Katahdin but lower than Mt. Elbert?

   A Cheaha Mountain

   B Mt. Mansfield

   C Humphreys Peak

   D Mt. Colorado

2. Use the digits 2, 4, 6, and 8. What is the greatest four-digit number you can form using each of the digits exactly once?

   A 2468

   B 6842

   C 8462

   D 8642

3. The Toronto Star had a circulation of 451,972 in 2005. What is that number rounded to the nearest hundred thousand?

   A 400,000

   B 450,000

   C 452,000

   D 500,000

4. Tomás played two games. He scored several points in the first game. He scored 3 points in the second game. Which expression shows how many points Tomás scored in the two games?

   A $n - 3$

   B $n + 3$

   C $3n$

   D $3 + 3$

5. Edgar went shopping. He bought a t-shirt for $19.95, shorts for $28.79, and socks for $3.85. How much did he spend in all?

   A $48.74

   B $50.00

   C $52.59

   D $52.69

6. Jin bought a DVD that costs $8.29. She paid with a $10 bill and got the correct change. Which shows the bills and coins she might have received?

   A 1 dollar, 3 quarters, 1 dime, 1 penny

   B 1 dollar, 2 quarters, 2 dimes, 1 penny

   C 1 dollar, 1 quarter, 3 dimes, 9 pennies

   D 4 quarters, 2 dimes, 1 penny

7. A two-act play is 98 minutes long. The second act is 42 minutes long. How long is the first act?

   A 140 minutes

   B 56 minutes

   C 46 minutes

   D 42 minutes

8. The Outdoor Arts and Crafts Fair had 57 craft exhibits, 21 art exhibits, and 34 clothing exhibits. About how many clothing and craft exhibits were there at the fair?

   A about 110

   B about 100

   C about 90

   D about 120

9. There are 172 fourth graders and 219 fifth graders at Public School 6. How many fourth and fifth graders are there altogether?

   A 452

   B 391

   C 381

   D 47

10. Ethan estimated the sum of 42,778 + 9045 by rounding each addend to its greatest place. Which shows the correct estimated sum of the two addends using Ethan's method?

    A 60,000

    B 51,000

    C 50,000

    D 49,000

11. Mr. Choi received 3487 votes for mayor. Ms. Miller got twice that number of votes. How many votes did Ms. Miller get?

    A 3489

    B 6874

    C 6974

    D 10,461

Circle the letter of the correct answer choice.

12. Mike and John are volunteers for the walk-a-thon. Mike gives out 303 pins. John gives out 245 pins. How many more pins does Mike give out than John?

A 48

B 58

C 68

D 548

13. Carmen used the distributive property to find 3 times the sum of 6 and 2. Which shows her calculation correctly?

A $(3 \times 6) + 2$

B $(3 \times 6) - (3 \times 2)$

C $(3 \times 6) \times (3 \times 2)$

D $(3 \times 6) + (3 \times 2)$

14. Keisha ran the 40-meter dash 6 times. How many meters did she run in all?

A 240 m

B 46 m

C 34 m

D 24 m

15. A football stadium has 58,006 seats. Ten thousand seats were added this year. How many seats does the stadium now have?

A 158,006

B 68,006

C 59,006

D 10,006

16. Ann made up a number riddle. Here are the clues:

- My number has 4 odd digits, all different.
- The thousands digit is 4 greater than the ones digits.
- The sum of the digits is 20.
- The sum of the middle two digits is 10.

Which could be Ann's number?

A 8444   C 7193

B 3917   D 7373

17. At Stereo Outlet, CD players sell for $79.99 each and speakers sell for $166 a pair. Howard's school purchased 4 CD players. About how much did the school spend in all?

A about $200   C about $320

B about $280   D about $400

18. Remi's book has 8 chapters. The average number of pages per chapter is 22. How many pages are in Remi's book?

A 166

B 176

C 186

D 276

19. Dawn is a printmaker. For her art show, she has 5 folders of 105 prints each and 2 folders of 75 prints each. How many prints does she have?

A 675

B 525

C 180

D 150

20. Abena bought twelve quarts of milk. Each quart costs $1.87. How much did she spend in all?

A $4.51

B $19.00

C $21.14

D $22.44

21. A new animated movie was shown 3 times on Saturday afternoon. The table shows how many tickets were sold for each showing.

Movie Time	Tickets Sold
12:25 P.M.	437
2:45 P.M.	528
5:05 P.M.	501

What is the difference between the greatest number of tickets sold and the least number sold?

A 965

B 91

C 74

D 27

22. Ben has 4 coins that total exactly $0.86. What are his coins?

A half dollar, dime, nickel, penny

B half dollar, quarter, dime, penny

C quarter, dime, nickel, penny

D 2 quarters, dime, nickel

Name _____

Circle the letter of the correct answer choice.

1. Which place-value chart shows the correct sum of three thousand sixty-five plus fourteen thousand four hundred twenty-seven?

Thousands Period			Ones Period		
Hundreds	Tens	Ones	Hundreds	Tens	Ones
	1	1	3	6	2

A

Thousands Period			Ones Period		
Hundreds	Tens	Ones	Hundreds	Tens	Ones
	1	8	0	0	7

C

Thousands Period			Ones Period		
Hundreds	Tens	Ones	Hundreds	Tens	Ones
	1	7	4	9	2

B

Thousands Period			Ones Period		
Hundreds	Tens	Ones	Hundreds	Tens	Ones
	4	4	4	9	2

D

2. Use each digit in the box only once. What two numbers can you form that have a sum of 527 and a difference of 375?

| 1 | 4 | 6 | 7 | 5 |

A 641 and 57

B 714 and 65

C 451 and 76

D 514 and 67

---

3. The table shows how much some animals might weigh.

Animal	Weight
Sheep	150 pounds
Fox	15 pounds
Horse	950 pounds
Beaver	60 pounds
Elephant	14,000 pounds

Which weighs more than 2 elephants?

A 20 horses + 50 sheep

B 100 foxes + 75 beavers + 10 sheep

C 25 horses + 25 beavers + 25 sheep

D 1 elephant + 10 horses + 100 foxes

4. A school bus carrying 39 students comes to a bus stop. No more students get on, but some of the students get off.

Which expression could be used to describe the situation?

A $39 - n$ **C** $39 + n$

B $39 \times n$ **D** $39 + 39$

---

5. The bar graph shows the number of points scored by a basketball team.

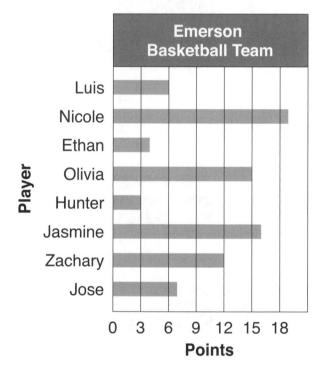

Which of the following is true?

A Hunter scored more points than Ethan.

B Olivia and Jasmine each scored more points than Nicole.

C The total of points scored by the team was about 80.

D Olivia scored 5 more points than Zachary.

Read the questions. Use the strategies to choose the answer choice that makes the most sense.

1. Cassidy uses 6 small tomatoes for each salad she makes. How many salads can she make with 54 tomatoes?

   A 6

   B 7

   C 9

   D 12

To find how many tomatoes, n, divide: $54 \div 6 = n$.

Remember: Division and multiplication are inverse operations, so you can use a related multiplication fact to solve for n.

• The related multiplication fact for $54 \div 6 = n$ is $6 \times n = 54$.

$$6 \times n = 54$$
$$n = 9$$

Think
$6 \times n = 54$
$6 \times 9 = 54$

So, $54 \div 6 = 9$

Answer choice C is correct.

2. Karen read a 265-page book in 5 days. She read the same number of pages each day. About how many pages did she read each day?

   A about 5 pages

   B about 50 pages

   C about 60 pages

   D about 100 pages

Think
You can estimate quotients before you divide.

• Find where the quotient begins. Try dividing hundreds.

   $5\overline{)265}$ $5 > 2$ Not enough hundreds

Try dividing tens.

   $5\overline{)265}$ $5 < 26$ Enough tens

So the quotient *begins* in the tens place.

• Find the first digit of the quotient. Think of a basic multiplication fact with a 5 whose product is close to 26, but not greater than 26.

   $5 \times 5 = 25$

Write a 5 in the tens place. Since you are estimating, write zeros for the other digits.

$$\frac{50}{5\overline{)265}}$$

Answer choice B is correct.

Name _____

Circle the letter of the correct answer choice.

3. **Which is a related division fact for $6 \times n = 24$?**

   A $6 \div 6 = 1$

   B $24 \div 4 = 6$

   C $24 \div 2 = 12$

   D $24 \div 3 = 8$

6. **Find the quotient.**

   $$84 \div 9 = \square$$

   A 7

   B 8 R 4

   C 9 R 3

   D 11

4. **Find the missing divisor.**

   $$48 \div c = 8$$

   A 6

   B 8

   C 12

   D 16

7. **Estimate the quotient.**

   $$9\overline{)4729}$$

   A about 50

   B about 300

   C about 500

   D about 5000

5. **There are 637 pencils in stock in the school supply store. Each box holds about 8 pencils. About how many boxes of pencils are in stock?**

   A about 7

   B about 70

   C about 95

   D about 120

8. **The divisor is 8. The quotient is 4. What is the dividend?**

   A 16

   B 24

   C 32

   D 40

Read the questions. Use the strategies to choose
the answer choice that makes the most sense.

STRATEGIES

1. **Which number is divisible by 3?**

   A 25

   B 26

   C 35

   D 60

   Remember:
   • A number is *divisible* by another number when you divide and the remainder is zero.
   • A number is divisible by **3** if the sum of the digits is divisible by **3**.

   • Find the sum of the digits of each answer choice. Divide the sum by 3.

   A: $25 \rightarrow 2 + 5 = 7 \rightarrow 7 \div 3 = 2 \text{ R } 1$

   B: $26 \rightarrow 2 + 6 = 8 \rightarrow 8 \div 3 = 2 \text{ R } 2$

   C: $35 \rightarrow 3 + 5 = 8 \rightarrow 8 \div 3 = 2 \text{ R } 2$

   D: $60 \rightarrow 6 + 0 = 6 \rightarrow 6 \div 3 = 2$

   D is the only choice that has a remainder of zero.

   Answer choice D is correct.

2. **Martha has collected 618 stamps in 6 months. She collected the same number of stamps each month. How many stamps did Martha collect each month?**

   A 3708

   B 130

   C 106

   D 103

   Think
   Divide 618 by 6 to find the number of stamps collected each month.

   • Divide the hundreds.
   $6 \times 1 = 6$, so write 1 in the hundreds place.

   $$\begin{array}{r} 1 \\ 6\overline{)618} \\ -6 \\ \hline \end{array}$$

   • Divide the tens.
   $6 > 1$, Not enough tens so write 0 in the tens place.

   $$\begin{array}{r} 10 \\ 6\overline{)618} \\ -6 \\ \hline 01 \end{array}$$

   • Divide the ones.
   $6 \times 3 = 18$, so write 3 in the ones place.

   $$\begin{array}{r} 103 \\ 6\overline{)618} \\ -6 \\ \hline 018 \\ -18 \\ \hline 0 \end{array}$$

   Answer choice D is correct.

Circle the letter of the correct answer choice.

3. **Which number is divisible by 3?**

   A 52

   B 163

   C 256

   D 309

4. **Find the quotient.**

   $$609 \div 4$$

   A 154 R2

   B 152 R1

   C 152

   D 151

5. **Sonia is arranging flowers for a party. Each arrangement will have 5 flowers. She does not want to have any flowers left over. How many flowers could she use to make 6 arrangements?**

   A 18

   B 21

   C 22

   D 30

6. **Jake cut an 80-inch wooden board into 5 equal-size pieces. How long is each piece?**

   A 75 inches

   B 18 inches

   C 16 inches

   D 5 inches

7. **Divide.**

   $$3\overline{)74}$$

   A 21 R1

   B 24

   C 24 R2

   D 25

8. **Find the quotient.**

   $$722 \div 7$$

   A 131

   B 130

   C 103 R1

   D 103

Read the questions. Use the strategies to choose the answer choice that makes the most sense.

STRATEGIES

1. What is the value of the expression?

$$4 \times 20 - 32 \div 8 + 8 = n$$

A 14

B 74

C 78

D 84

Think
You can use the *order of operations*.

• First multiply and divide.

$$4 \times 20 - 32 \div 8 + 8$$
$$80 \quad - \quad 4 \quad + 8$$

Remember: Work in order from left to right.

• Then add and subtract.

$$80 - 4 + 8$$
$$76 \quad + 8 = 84$$

Answer choice D is correct.

2. Which student had the greatest mean, or average, test score?

Student	Test A	Test B	Test C	Test D
Ben	72	85	77	98
Sara	88	96	94	90
Sam	92	90	82	92
Ari	93	89	87	91

A Ben

B Sara

C Sam

D Ari

Think
To find the *mean*, add the test scores. Then divide the sum by the number of test scores.

• Mean of Ben's scores: $72 + 85 + 77 + 98 = 332$ $332 \div 4 = \mathbf{83}$

• Mean of Sara's scores: $88 + 96 + 94 + 90 = 368$ $368 \div 4 = \mathbf{92}$

• Mean of Sam's scores: $92 + 90 + 82 + 92 = 356$ $356 \div 4 = \mathbf{89}$

• Mean of Ari's scores: $93 + 89 + 87 + 91 = 360$ $360 \div 4 = \mathbf{90}$

Answer choice B is correct.

3. Eli, Lindsay, and Brian have 1750 stamps. If they share the stamps equally, how many stamps are left over?

A 10

B 9

C 1

D 0

```
      583 R1
  3)1750
   -15
     25
    -24
     10
   -  9
      1
```

The remainder of 1 means that there is 1 stamp left over.

Answer choice C is correct.

Circle the letter of the correct answer choice.

4. Four friends evenly shared the cost of a pizza and four salads. The pizza costs $16 and the salads cost $1.80 each. How much did each friend pay?

   A $4

   B $4.45

   C $5.80

   D $17.80

5. What is the value of the expression?

   $$400 \div 5 \times 4 - 16 + 3 = n$$

   A 1   **C** 147

   B 7   **D** 307

6. Arlo, Bonita, Cara, and Daniel recorded the number of laps they swam at swim practice one week. On which day was the mean number of laps the greatest?

Student	Mon.	Tues.	Wed.	Thurs.
Arlo	31	40	34	30
Bonita	36	32	34	32
Cara	34	30	32	36
Daniel	35	30	30	32

   A Monday   **C** Wednesday

   B Tuesday   **D** Thursday

7. The baking club made 114 carrot muffins. The club has 8 members. How many more muffins do they need to share the muffins equally?

   A 2   **C** 6

   B 4   **D** 12

8. What is the remainder when you divide 28,845 by 8?

   A 6

   B 5

   C 3

   D No remainder

9. What is the mean?

   $4.72, $3.19, 6.05, $5.20

   A $4.84

   B $4.79

   C $4.29

   D $4.09

10. Which expression has a value of 16?

   A $200 \div 8 - 5$

   B $14 \times 4 \div 7 \times 8 - 58$

   C $18 + 6 \times 2 - 11 + 6$

   D $2 \times 2 \times 2 \times 2$

Read the questions. Use the strategies to choose
the answer choice that makes the most sense.

STRATEGIES

1. **Carter is a running back on the football team. On the first down, he runs 4 yd 2 ft. On the second down, he runs 2 yd 2 ft. What is the total distance Carter runs?**

   A 2 yd 2 ft   **C** 7 yd 1 ft

   B 6 yd 2 ft   **D** 7 yd 2 ft

Add to find the total distance.

• Add the smaller units first. Rename units as needed.

> Remember:
> 3 ft = 1 yd

$$\begin{array}{r} 4 \text{ yd } 2 \text{ ft} \\ + \ 2 \text{ yd } 2 \text{ ft} \\ \hline \end{array}$$

6 yd 4 ft = 6 yd + **1 yd + 1 ft** = 7 yd 1 ft

> 4 ft = 3 ft + 1 ft
>   = **1 yd + 1 ft**

Answer choice C is correct.

2. **Amy painted a mural at the playground. She used one color more than any other. Which color is that?**

red	yellow	green	blue
2 qt	10 pt	4 qt	6 qt

   A red   **C** green

   B yellow   **D** blue

Rename all units as pints.

> Remember:
> 1 qt = 2 pt

• Multiply to rename larger units as smaller units.

2 qt red = 2 × 2 pt   = 4 pt red
10 pt yellow   = 10 pt yellow
4 qt green = 4 × 2 pt = 8 pt green
6 qt blue = 6 × 2 pt = 12 pt blue

4 pt < 8 pt < 10 pt < 12 pt

Answer choice D is correct.

3. **Which is the most reasonable estimate for the weight of a notebook?**

   A about 1 T

   B about 1 oz

   C about 1 lb

   D about 100 lb

> **Think**
> You can use familiar objects, or **benchmarks**, to help you estimate weight.

• A small car weighs about 1 ton (T).

• A letter that you mail weighs about 1 ounce (oz).

• 1 pound (lb) = 16 oz

Answer choice C is correct.

Circle the letter of the correct answer choice.

4. The fence around Ms. Lee's garden is 78 ft long. How many yards long is the fence?

   A 26 yd

   B 75 yd

   C 81 yd

   D 234 yd

5. Justin packed five boxes of ribbon. Each box weighed 1 lb. How many ounces did all the boxes weigh?

   A 16 oz

   B 21 oz

   C 50 oz

   D 80 oz

6. Subtract.

$$\begin{array}{r} 8 \text{ ft } 6 \text{ in.} \\ -\ 2 \text{ ft } 4 \text{ in.} \\ \hline \end{array}$$

   A 4 ft 2 in.

   B 6 ft 2 in.

   C 6 ft 10 in.

   D 10 ft 10 in.

7. How many cups are in 5 quarts?

   A 80 cups

   B 40 cups

   C 20 cups

   D 10 cups

8. Brandon knit a scarf that was 3 yards long. How many inches long was the scarf?

   A 18 in.

   B 36 in.

   C 72 in.

   D 108 in.

9. If a bicycle weighs about 42 lb, which is the most reasonable estimate for the weight of a school bus?

   A about 5 lb

   B about 5 T

   C about 5 oz

   D about 50 lb

Read the questions. Use the strategies to choose
the answer choice that makes the most sense.

STRATEGIES

1. **Which shows the lengths in order from shortest to longest?**

   A 6000 cm, 80 dm, 40 m

   B 40 m, 80 dm, 6000 cm

   C 80 dm, 40 m, 6000 cm

   D 80 dm, 6000 cm, 40 m

• Rename all units as meters.

• Divide to rename smaller units as larger units.

Remember:
100 centimeters (cm) = 1 meter (m)
10 decimeters (dm) = 1 meter (m)

6000 cm = 6000 cm ÷ 100 = **60 m**

80 dm = 80 dm ÷ 10 = **8 m**

40 m = **40 m**

$$8 \text{ m} < 40 \text{ m} < 60 \text{ m}$$
$$\downarrow \qquad \downarrow \qquad \downarrow$$
$$80 \text{ dm} < 40 \text{ m} < 6000 \text{ cm}$$

Answer choice C is correct.

2. **What is the most reasonable estimate for the mass of a dictionary?**

   A about 2 g

   B about 12 g

   C about 2 kg

   D about 1000 kg

.Think.
You can use familiar objects, or **benchmarks**, to help you estimate mass.

• A paper clip has a mass of about 1 gram (g).

• A textbook has a mass of about 1 kilogram (kg).

Remember:
1000 g = 1 kg

Answer choice C is correct.

Circle the letter of the correct answer choice.

3. Brian walked from his house to the library and back. The distance from his house to the library is 1 kilometer. Which shows the distance Brian walked?

   A 1000 m

   B 2000 dm

   C 2000 m

   D 4000 mm

4. Emily drinks 4 liters of water each day. How many milliliters of water does she drink?
   Hint: 1000 mL = 1L

   A 4 mL

   B 40 mL

   C 400 mL

   D 4000 mL

5. Which shows the masses in order from greatest to least?
   Hint: 1000 g = 1 kg

   A 2000 kg, 6000 g, 4 kg

   B 2000 kg, 4 kg, 6000 g

   C 6000 g, 2000 kg, 4 kg

   D 4 kg, 2000 kg, 6000 g

6. Which of the following might weigh about 10 kg?

   A a dog

   B a mouse

   C an elephant

   D a car

7. Which unit would you use to measure the distance from Massachusetts to Florida?

   A millimeters

   B meters

   C kilometers

   D decimeters

8. Alex mixed 850 mL of orange juice with 1150 mL of cranberry juice. How many liters of punch did he make?

   A 2000 L

   B 200 L

   C 20 L

   D 2 L

Read the questions. Use the strategies to choose the answer choice that makes the most sense.

STRATEGIES

1. **Each day, Greg practices piano from 15 minutes past 3 in the afternoon to 4:00 P.M. How long does Greg practice in one week?**

   A 45 minutes

   B 4 hours 45 minutes

   C 5 hours 15 minutes

   D 5 hours 50 minutes

Think
15 minutes past 3 in the afternoon is 3:15 P.M.

- Draw a clock that shows 3:15.
- Start at 3. Count quarter hours to 4.00.

Remember: There are 15 minutes in one quarter hour.

Greg practices for 45 minutes each day.

- To find how long Greg practices in 1 week, or 7 days.

   7×45 minutes $= 315$ minutes

   60 minutes $= 1$ hour
   300 minutes $= 5$ hours
   315 minutes $= 5$ hours 15 minutes

Answer choice C is correct.

2. **The temperature rose 3° per hour from 9:00 A.M. to noon. It was 20°C at noon. What was the temperature at 9:00 A.M.?**

   A 9°   **C** 21°

   B 11°   **D** 29°

Think
The temperature was 20°C at noon. If the temperature rose from 9:00 A.M. to noon, then the temperature at 9:00 A.M. was less than 20°C.

- There are 3 hours from 9:00 A.M. to noon. The temperature rose 3° per hour.
   $3 \times 3 = 9$
- The temperature rose 9°.
- Subtract to find the temperature at 9:00 A.M.
   $20 - 9 = 11$

Answer choice B, 11°, is correct.

Circle the letter of the correct answer choice.

3. 2 hours 25 minutes = □ minutes

   A 60

   B 85

   C 135

   D 145

4. The temperature was 65°F at 7:00 P.M. It dropped by 8° by 10:00 P.M. What was the temperature at 10:00 P.M.?

   A 57° F

   B 63° F

   C 67° F

   D 73° F

5. Which shows the time at 14 minutes to 10 at night?

   A 9:46 A.M.

   B 10:14 A.M.

   C 9:46 P.M.

   D 10:14 P.M.

6. How many minutes are in 4 hours?

   A 24

   B 60

   C 240

   D 300

7. How many minutes pass from 11:28 P.M. to 12:02 A.M.?

   A 30 minutes

   B 32 minutes

   C 34 minutes

   D 44 minutes

8. Pilar and Max plan to visit a state park that is 1 hour and 40 minutes away. They want to get there at 2:00 P.M. What time should they leave?

   A 12:20 A.M.

   B 12:20 P.M.

   C 1:20 P.M.

   D 3:40 P.M.

9. Which is the best estimate for the temperature on a hot summer day?

   A 10°C

   B 10°F

   C 90°C

   D 90°F

Read the questions. Use the strategies to choose
the answer choice that makes the most sense.

STRATEGIES

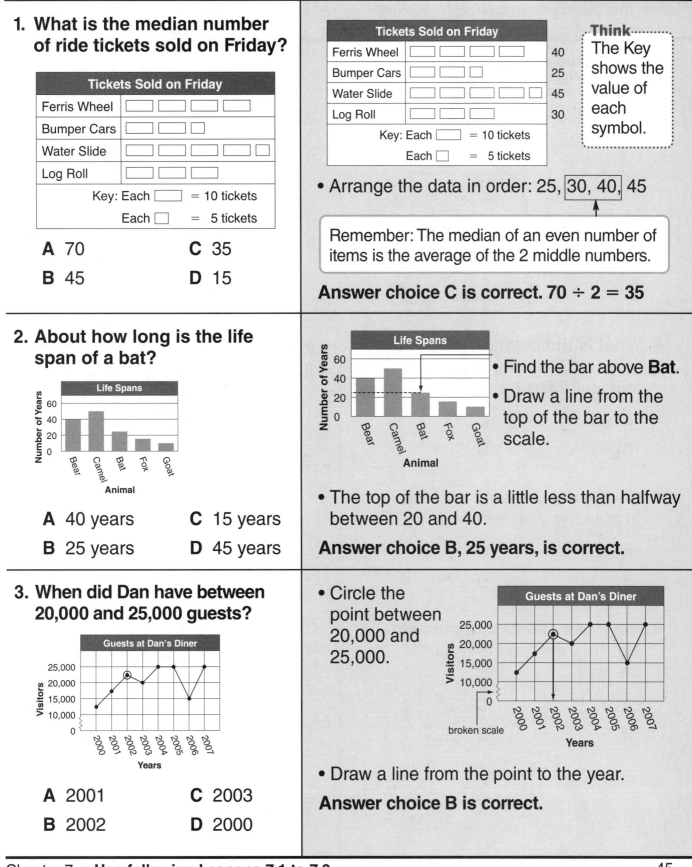

1. What is the median number of ride tickets sold on Friday?

Tickets Sold on Friday				
Ferris Wheel	☐	☐	☐	☐
Bumper Cars	☐	☐	☐	
Water Slide	☐	☐	☐	☐☐
Log Roll	☐	☐	☐	

Key: Each ☐ = 10 tickets
Each ☐ = 5 tickets

A 70   **C** 35

B 45   **D** 15

Tickets Sold on Friday					
Ferris Wheel	☐	☐	☐	☐	40
Bumper Cars	☐	☐	☐		25
Water Slide	☐	☐	☐	☐☐	45
Log Roll	☐	☐	☐		30

Key: Each ☐ = 10 tickets
Each ☐ = 5 tickets

Think The Key shows the value of each symbol.

• Arrange the data in order: 25, 30, 40, 45

Remember: The median of an even number of items is the average of the 2 middle numbers.

Answer choice C is correct. 70 ÷ 2 = 35

2. About how long is the life span of a bat?

Life Spans

Number of Years (Bear, Camel, Bat, Fox, Goat)

Animal

A 40 years   **C** 15 years

B 25 years   **D** 45 years

Life Spans

Number of Years (Bear, Camel, Bat, Fox, Goat)

Animal

• Find the bar above **Bat**.

• Draw a line from the top of the bar to the scale.

• The top of the bar is a little less than halfway between 20 and 40.

Answer choice B, 25 years, is correct.

3. When did Dan have between 20,000 and 25,000 guests?

Guests at Dan's Diner

Visitors (25,000 / 20,000 / 15,000 / 10,000 / 0)

Years (2000–2007)

A 2001   **C** 2003

B 2002   **D** 2000

• Circle the point between 20,000 and 25,000.

Guests at Dan's Diner

Visitors (25,000 / 20,000 / 15,000 / 10,000 / 0)

broken scale

Years (2000–2007)

• Draw a line from the point to the year.

Answer choice B is correct.

Circle the letter of the correct answer choice.

Use the pictograph below to answer questions 4 through 6.

Students Learning a Musical Instrument

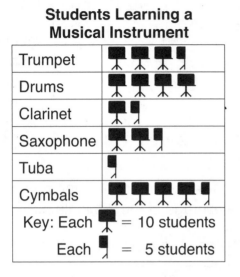

4. **What is the median number of students learning to play a musical instrument?**

   A 20   **C** 30

   B 45   **D** 5

5. **How many students are learning to play the clarinet?**

   A 15   **C** 20

   B 25   **D** 2

6. **How many fewer students are learning the tuba than the drums?**

   A 45   **C** 35

   B 3   **D** 15

7. **Look at the bar graph below.**

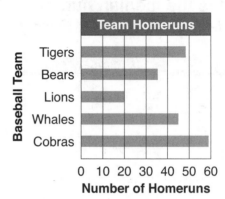

   Which team scored about 14 fewer homeruns than the Cobras?

   A Tigers   **C** Whales

   B Bears   **D** Lions

8. **Look at the line graph below.**

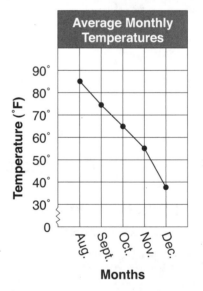

   Between which two months was the drop in temperature greatest?

   A August and September

   B September and October

   C October and November

   D November and December

Read the questions. Use the strategies to choose the answer choice that makes the most sense.

STRATEGIES

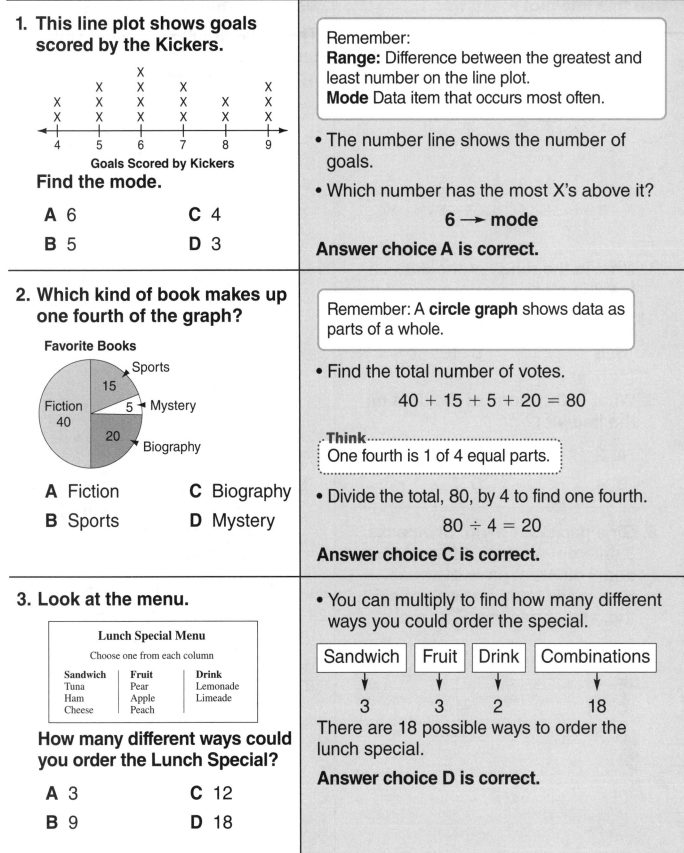

1. This line plot shows goals scored by the Kickers.

Goals Scored by Kickers

Find the mode.

A 6   **C** 4

B 5   **D** 3

Remember:
Range: Difference between the greatest and least number on the line plot.
Mode Data item that occurs most often.

• The number line shows the number of goals.

• Which number has the most X's above it?

$$6 \rightarrow \text{mode}$$

Answer choice A is correct.

2. Which kind of book makes up one fourth of the graph?

Favorite Books

Sports
15
Fiction 40
5 Mystery
20
Biography

A Fiction   **C** Biography

B Sports   **D** Mystery

Remember: A **circle graph** shows data as parts of a whole.

• Find the total number of votes.

$$40 + 15 + 5 + 20 = 80$$

Think
One fourth is 1 of 4 equal parts.

• Divide the total, 80, by 4 to find one fourth.

$$80 \div 4 = 20$$

Answer choice C is correct.

3. Look at the menu.

Lunch Special Menu

Choose one from each column

Sandwich	**Fruit**	**Drink**
Tuna	Pear	Lemonade
Ham	Apple	Limeade
Cheese	Peach	

How many different ways could you order the Lunch Special?

A 3   **C** 12

B 9   **D** 18

• You can multiply to find how many different ways you could order the special.

Sandwich	Fruit	Drink	Combinations
3	3	2	18

There are 18 possible ways to order the lunch special.

Answer choice D is correct.

Name _____

Circle the letter of the correct answer choice.

Use this line plot to answer questions 4 and 5.

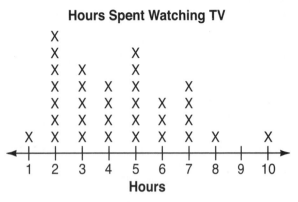

Hours Spent Watching TV

4. What is the range of the data on the line plot?

A 2   C 9

B 5   D 10

5. What is the mode of the data on the line plot?

A 2   C 5

B 4   D 7

6. Gina packs for a trip. She packs 3 different skirts, 5 different tops, and 3 different pairs of shoes. How many combinations of skirt, top, and shoes can Gina make?

A 45

B 24

C 11

D 3

Use the graph for questions 7–8.

The circle graph shows the kind of instruments the members of a junior symphony orchestra play.

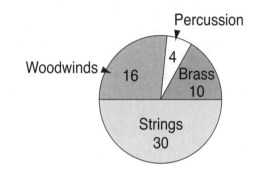

7. Which kind of instrument is played by ten members of the orchestra?

A Percussion

B Brass

C Woodwinds

D Strings

8. Which two kinds of instruments together make up one third of all the instruments orchestra members play?

A Percussion and Brass

B Strings and Percussion

C Woodwinds and Percussion

D Brass and Woodwinds

Read the questions. Use the strategies to choose the answer choice that makes the most sense.

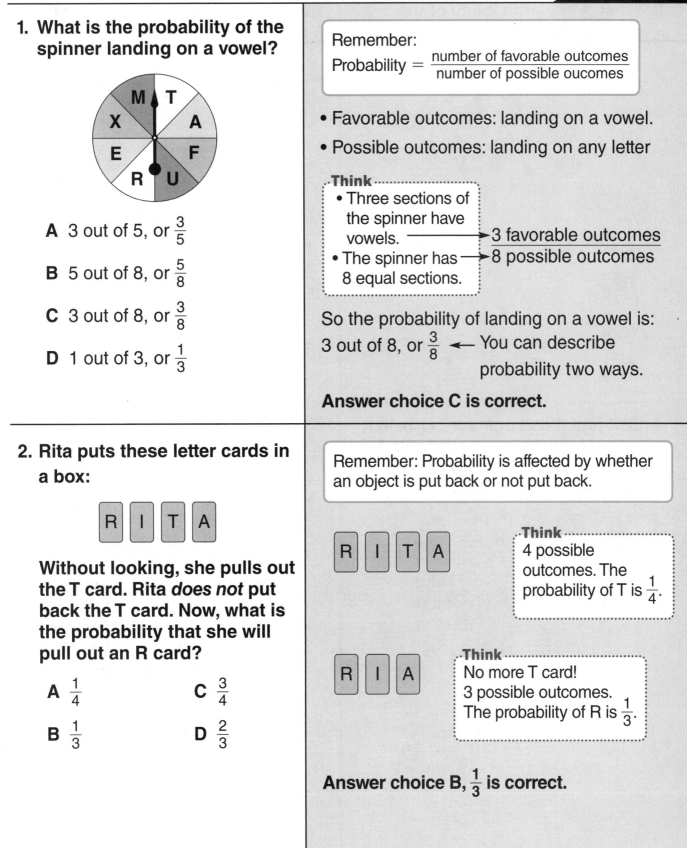

1. What is the probability of the spinner landing on a vowel?

   A 3 out of 5, or $\frac{3}{5}$

   B 5 out of 8, or $\frac{5}{8}$

   C 3 out of 8, or $\frac{3}{8}$

   D 1 out of 3, or $\frac{1}{3}$

Remember:
Probability = $\frac{\text{number of favorable outcomes}}{\text{number of possible oucomes}}$

• Favorable outcomes: landing on a vowel.

• Possible outcomes: landing on any letter

Think
• Three sections of the spinner have vowels. ⟶ 3 favorable outcomes
• The spinner has ⟶ 8 possible outcomes 8 equal sections.

So the probability of landing on a vowel is:
3 out of 8, or $\frac{3}{8}$ ⟵ You can describe probability two ways.

Answer choice C is correct.

2. Rita puts these letter cards in a box:

   R I T A

   Without looking, she pulls out the T card. Rita *does not* put back the T card. Now, what is the probability that she will pull out an R card?

   A $\frac{1}{4}$ C $\frac{3}{4}$

   B $\frac{1}{3}$ D $\frac{2}{3}$

Remember: Probability is affected by whether an object is put back or not put back.

R I T A

Think
4 possible outcomes. The probability of T is $\frac{1}{4}$.

R I A

Think
No more T card! 3 possible outcomes. The probability of R is $\frac{1}{3}$.

Answer choice B, $\frac{1}{3}$ is correct.

Circle the letter of the correct answer choice.

3. What is the probability of the spinner landing on an odd number?

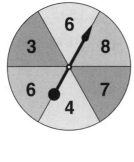

A $\frac{3}{5}$

B $\frac{5}{8}$

C $\frac{2}{6}$

D $\frac{1}{6}$

4. Carl has these number cards in a box. If he pulls out 1 card without looking, which number is he most likely to pull out?

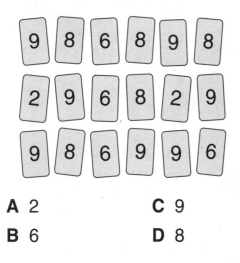

A 2   C 9

B 6   D 8

Use this number cube for questions 5 and 6.

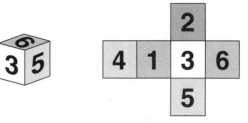

5. What is the probability of rolling a 3?

A 3 out of 6   C 1 out of 6

B 5 out of 6   D 1 out of 3

6. What is the probability of rolling a 9?

A $\frac{0}{6}$ C $\frac{1}{9}$

B $\frac{1}{6}$ D $\frac{8}{9}$

7. These checkers are in a bag.

Without looking you pull out a white checker and put it in your pocket. Then you pull out another checker without looking. What is the probability of pulling out another white checker?

A $\frac{1}{7}$ C $\frac{2}{6}$

B $\frac{3}{6}$ D $\frac{4}{7}$

Read the problem. Use the Problem-Solving Guide below to help you think about the answer choices.

In 98 days, Kim's dog Spot gained 21 pounds. How many weeks did it take Spot to gain the weight?

A 3 weeks   **C** 14 weeks

B 11 weeks   **D** 686 weeks

PROBLEM-SOLVING GUIDE

① Understand the Question

- The question is asking you to find the answer choice that shows how long it took Spot to gain a certain amount of weight.

- Each answer choice shows a different amount of weeks.

- The fact that Spot gained 21 pounds is extra information that is not needed to solve the problem.

② Understand Word Meanings

- When you **gain** something, you come to have more of it. A pound is a measure of weight. To gain pounds means to have more weight.

- The words **how long** tell you that you need to find a total amount of time that it took Spot to gain that weight. You must give the time in weeks, not days.

③ Understand How to Solve

- Reread the question if you need to.

- Choose the operation to find how many weeks equal 98 days.

- A week is a greater unit than a day. Divide to find the number of weeks.

$$\frac{14}{7 \overline{)98}}$$

Think
1 week = 7 days

Remember: When you rename units of measure, divide to rename a smaller unit as a larger one.

④ Circle the Letter of the Correct Answer Choice.

Answer choice C is correct.
Spot gained the weight in 14 weeks.

Name _____

Circle the letter of the correct answer choice.

The old centerfield fence of a baseball field was 410 feet 8 inches from home plate. The new centerfield fence is 2 feet 8 inches farther from home plate. How far from home plate is the new centerfield fence?

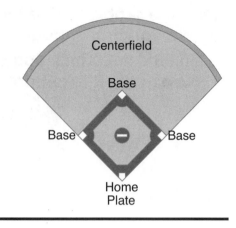

A 2 ft 8 in. **C** 412 ft 4 in.

B 408 ft **D** 413 ft 4 in.

Complete each sentence.

① Understand the Question

• The new fence is _____ from home plate than the old fence was.

• You need to find the distance of the new fence from _____.

② Understand Word Meanings: farther

• You know the meaning of the root word far.
• You know the suffix –er means "more."
• What do you think is the meaning of farther? _____

③ Understand How to Solve

• To find how far from home plate, add 410 ft 8 in. and 2 ft 8 in. more.

```
    410 ft   8 in.
 +    2 ft   8 in.
    412 ft  16 in.
```

Remember: 12 in. = 1 ft

• Rename 16 in. as _____ ft _____ in.

• 412 ft + 1 ft + 4 in. = _____ ft _____ in.

④ Circle the Letter of the Correct Answer Choice.

Answer Choice _____ is correct. The new centerfield fence is

_____ from home plate.

Circle the letter of the correct answer choice.

1. **Kelly and her three friends are sharing fruit. How can they share 24 plums equally?**

   A 4 each

   B 6 each

   C 8 each

   D 27 each

2. **Taylor hid 58 cards all over the house. If each of 6 children found the same number of cards, what is the greatest number of cards each child could have found? How many cards would remain hidden?**

   A 10 cards found, 0 still hidden

   B 9 cards found, 4 still hidden

   C 9 cards found, 2 still hidden

   D 8 cards found, 10 still hidden

3. **Carl says that 20 is divisible only by 2, 4, 5, and 10. Suki says it is divisible only by 2 and 10. Ivan says 20 is divisible by 1, 2, 4, 5, 10, and 20. And Claire claims that it is divisible only by 1 and 20. Who is right?**

   A Carl   **C** Ivan

   B Suki   **D** Claire

4. **Dan cut a 64-inch board into 4 equal parts. It took him 2 minutes to make each cut. How long is each part?**

   A 12 in.

   B 1 ft 3 in.

   C 1 ft 4 in.

   D 1 ft 5 in.

5. **For every quarter that Lin saves, her aunt will give her a dollar. How much money will Lin have if she saves 4 quarters?**

   A $8.00

   B $5.00

   C $4.25

   D $1.00

6. **At Harvey's Hardware Store, there were 122 flashlights in stock. If Harvey sold the same number of flashlights in each of 5 weeks, what is the greatest number of flashlights he could have sold each week?**

   A 20

   B 22

   C 24

   D 25

7. Henry scored the following points in a basketball game:

18 4 8 10 15

What is the median of this set of data?

A 8

B 10

C 11

D 15

8. The parking lot for a movie theater is 54 yards wide and 40 yards long. How many feet wide is the parking lot?

A 18

B 120

C 162

D 282

9. A giraffe can run 32 miles in an hour. If it can keep up that speed, how long would it take a giraffe to run 96 miles?

A 3 hours

B 30 hours

C 64 hours

D 96 hours

10. Kayla's garage is 18 feet from her house. Huri's garage and house are 14 feet 9 inches apart. What is the difference in those two distances?

A 4 ft 9 in.

B 4 ft 1 in.

C 3 ft 9 in.

D 3 ft 3 in.

11. On 5 math tests, Beatrice got scores of 76, 83, 90, 85, and 86. What was her mean score?

A 84

B 85

C 90

D 105

12. A DVD of a popular TV series is 2 hours long. The DVD has 4 episodes, each the same length. How long is each episode?

A 120 min

B 80 min

C 60 min

D 30 min

Circle the letter of the correct answer choice.

13. The bar graph shows sales of dog food for a week at one large supermarket.

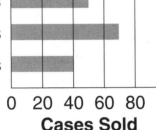

Dog Food Sales

How many more cases of Dog Delights were sold than cases of Puppy Pops?

A 10

B 20

C 30

D 40

14. Dawn's Diner offers a 3-part breakfast special. You can have orange, cranberry, or grapefruit juice to start. You can have eggs, hot cereal, or pancakes. You can have coffee or milk to drink. How many different ways can you order Dawn's breakfast special?

A 3   **C** 9

B 8   **D** 18

15. Tim rolls a cube with the letters A, B, C, D, E, and F on its six faces. What is the probability that he will roll a vowel?

A 1 out of 6

B 2 out of 6

C 4 out of 6

D 6 out of 6

16. Four friends met Saturday morning. Rolf left his house at 8:45 A.M. Rita left hers at 20 minutes to 9:00 A.M. Rosa left at 30 minutes past 8:00 A.M. Rune left at 15 minutes past 9:00 A.M. Who left home the earliest?

A Rune   **C** Rolf

B Rita   **D** Rosa

17. Pia bought 6 identical plants to give as gifts. She spent a total of $113.70. What did each plant cost?

A $18.90

B $18.95

C $19.00

D $682.22

18. A table tennis net is 15.25 centimeters wide and about 1.5 meters long. About how many centimeters long is the net?

 A about 2 cm **C** about 150 cm

 B about 15 cm **D** about 250 cm

19. Miguel and Diana left the train station at 11:50 P.M. It took them 32 minutes to get home from there. At what time did they get home?

 A 12:22 P.M. **C** 12:12 P.M.

 B 12:22 A.M. **D** 1:32 P.M.

20. The table shows the temperatures during one day.

Time	Temperature
10:00 A.M.	26°F
1:00 P.M.	31°F
4:00 P.M.	33°F
7:00 P.M.	32°F
10:00 P.M.	29°F

At what times was the temperature below freezing ?
Hint: Water freezes at 32°F.

 A 10:00 A.M. and 10:00 P.M.

 B 10:00 A.M., 1:00 P.M., 10:00 P.M.

 C 10:00 A.M., 1:00 P.M., 7:00 P.M., and 10:00 P.M.

 D 4:00 P.M. and 7:00 P.M.

21. Use the circle graph.

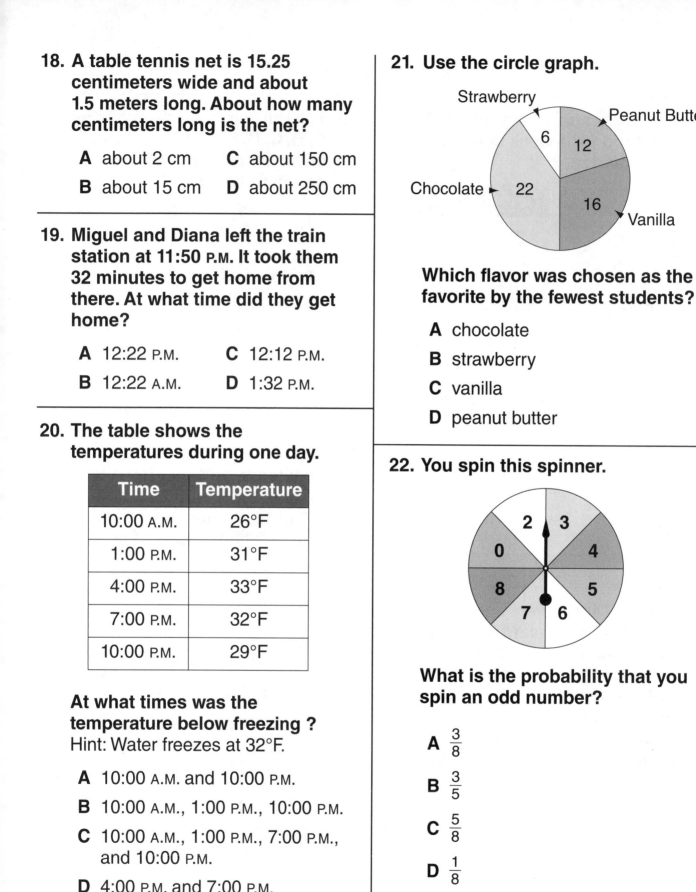

Which flavor was chosen as the favorite by the fewest students?

 A chocolate

 B strawberry

 C vanilla

 D peanut butter

22. You spin this spinner.

What is the probability that you spin an odd number?

 A $\frac{3}{8}$

 B $\frac{3}{5}$

 C $\frac{5}{8}$

 D $\frac{1}{8}$

57

Name _____

Circle the letter of the correct answer choice.

1. Some friends order 4 kinds of pizza. Twice as many people order sausage pizza than cheese pizza. There is one more order of cheese pizza than vegetable pizza. Two more people order vegetable pizza than mushroom pizza. Only one person orders mushroom pizza. Which circle graph shows the fraction of people that ordered vegetable pizza?

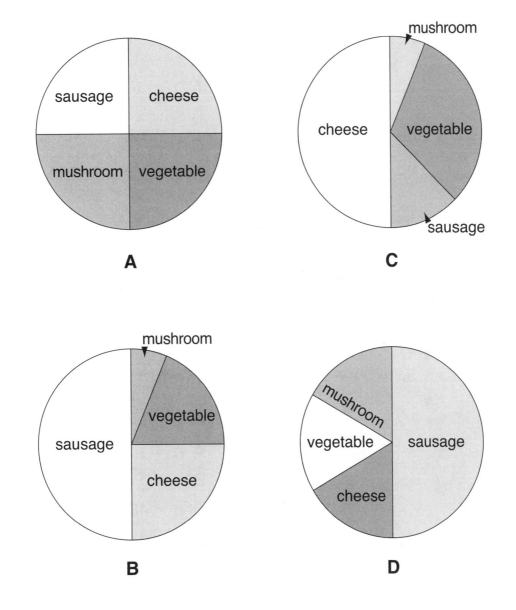

A

C

B

D

2. Meg puts these cards in a bag. Without looking, she pulls out one card.

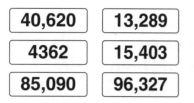

40,620	13,289
4362	15,403
85,090	96,327

What is the probability that the card Meg pulls out has a number that is divisible by 3?

A $\frac{1}{6}$

B $\frac{1}{2}$

C $\frac{2}{3}$

D $\frac{1}{3}$

3. A 3-digit number and a 1-digit number have a sum of 198, a difference of 180, and a product of 1701. What is the quotient of the two numbers?

A 210

B 189

C 21

D 9

4. The line plot shows the number of times that the temperature reached 80°F during a 5-month period. What was the mean number of 80-degree days in June, July, and August?

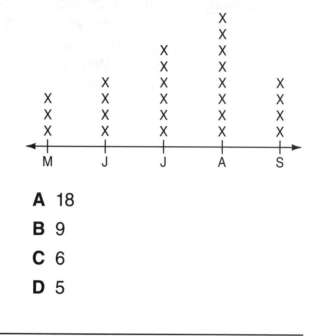

A 18

B 9

C 6

D 5

5. Which value of n will make the two sides of the scale weigh the same amount?

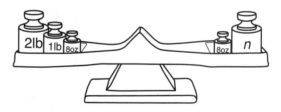

A n = 16 oz

B n = 1 lb

C n = 48 oz

D n = 4 lb

Read the questions. Use the strategies to choose the answer choice that makes the most sense.

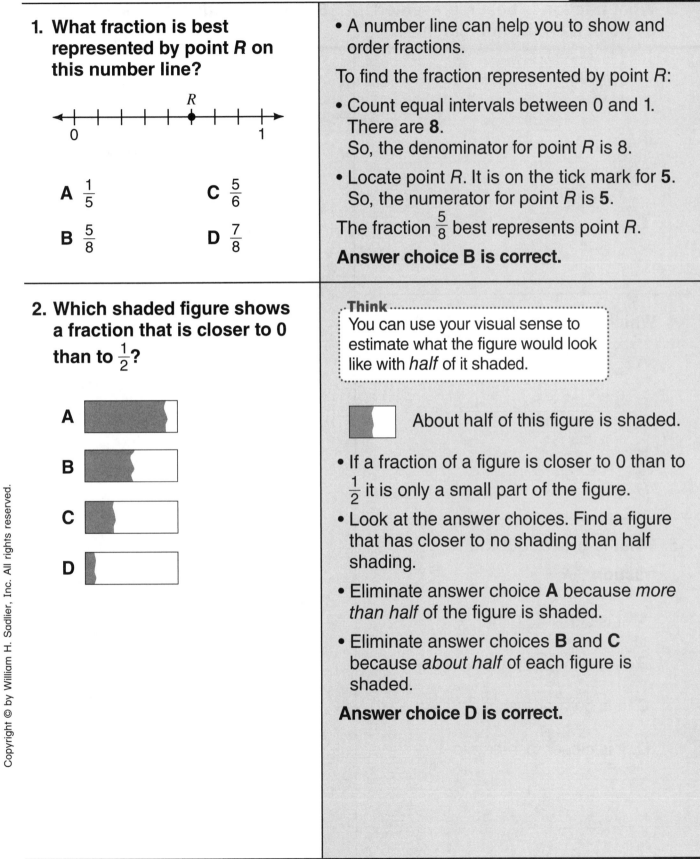

1. What fraction is best represented by point *R* on this number line?

A $\frac{1}{5}$ C $\frac{5}{6}$

B $\frac{5}{8}$ D $\frac{7}{8}$

STRATEGIES

• A number line can help you to show and order fractions.

To find the fraction represented by point *R*:

• Count equal intervals between 0 and 1. There are **8**.
So, the denominator for point *R* is 8.

• Locate point *R*. It is on the tick mark for **5**. So, the numerator for point *R* is 5.

The fraction $\frac{5}{8}$ best represents point *R*.

Answer choice B is correct.

2. Which shaded figure shows a fraction that is closer to 0 than to $\frac{1}{2}$?

A

B

C

D

Think

You can use your visual sense to estimate what the figure would look like with *half* of it shaded.

About half of this figure is shaded.

• If a fraction of a figure is closer to 0 than to $\frac{1}{2}$ it is only a small part of the figure.

• Look at the answer choices. Find a figure that has closer to no shading than half shading.

• Eliminate answer choice **A** because *more than half* of the figure is shaded.

• Eliminate answer choices **B** and **C** because *about half* of each figure is shaded.

Answer choice D is correct.

Name _____

Circle the letter of the correct answer choice.

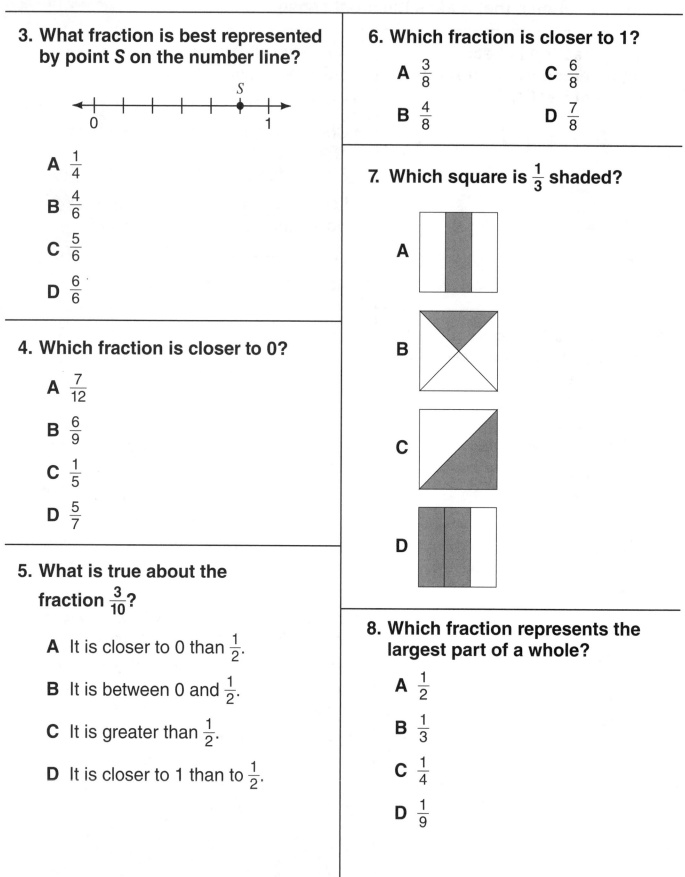

3. What fraction is best represented by point *S* on the number line?

A $\frac{1}{4}$

B $\frac{4}{6}$

C $\frac{5}{6}$

D $\frac{6}{6}$

4. Which fraction is closer to 0?

A $\frac{7}{12}$

B $\frac{6}{9}$

C $\frac{1}{5}$

D $\frac{5}{7}$

5. What is true about the fraction $\frac{3}{10}$?

A It is closer to 0 than $\frac{1}{2}$.

B It is between 0 and $\frac{1}{2}$.

C It is greater than $\frac{1}{2}$.

D It is closer to 1 than to $\frac{1}{2}$.

6. Which fraction is closer to 1?

A $\frac{3}{8}$ **C** $\frac{6}{8}$

B $\frac{4}{8}$ **D** $\frac{7}{8}$

7. Which square is $\frac{1}{3}$ shaded?

A

B

C

D

8. Which fraction represents the largest part of a whole?

A $\frac{1}{2}$

B $\frac{1}{3}$

C $\frac{1}{4}$

D $\frac{1}{9}$

Read the questions. Use the strategies to choose
the answer choice that makes the most sense.

1. **Find the missing number to complete the equivalent fraction.**

$$\frac{2}{4} = \frac{n}{12}$$

A 5   **C** 8

B 7   **D** 6

Remember: Equivalent fractions name the same part of a region or a set.

- Multiply the numerator and the denominator by the same number, 3.

$$\text{numerator} \longrightarrow \frac{2 \times 3}{4 \times 3} = \frac{6}{12}$$
$$\text{denominator} \longrightarrow$$

Think
$4 \times 3 = 12$

Answer choice D is correct.

2. **What is the greatest common factor (GCF) of 12 and 24?**

A 2   **C** 6
B 8   **D** 12

Two or more numbers that are multiplied to give a product are called *factors*.

- You can use multiplication sentences to find all the factors of 12 and 24.

$1 \times 12 = 12$	$1 \times 24 = 24$
$2 \times 6 = 12$	$2 \times 12 = 24$
$3 \times 4 = 12$	$3 \times 8 = 24$
	$4 \times 6 = 24$

- Find the *common factors* of 12 and 24:
  1, 2, 3, 4, 6, 12

The *greatest common factor* is 12.

Answer choice D is correct.

3. **What is the fraction $\frac{16}{24}$ in simplest form?**

A $\frac{1}{2}$ **C** $\frac{2}{3}$

B $\frac{3}{4}$ **D** $\frac{8}{12}$

Think
Factors of 16: 1, 2, 4, **8**, 16
Factors of 24: 1, 2, 3, 4, 6, **8**, 12, 24
The **GCF** of 16 and 24 is **8**.

- Divide the numerator and the denominator by their GCF. $\frac{16 \div 8}{24 \div 8} = \frac{2}{3}$

Answer choice C is correct.

Name _____

Circle the letter of the correct answer choice.

4. Which list shows the factors of 32?

A 2, 4, 8, 16

B 1, 2, 4, 8, 16, 32

C 1, 2, 3, 4, 6, 8, 16, 32

D 1, 2, 3, 4, 8, 16, 24, 32

5. Find the equivalent fraction.

$$\frac{s}{9} = \frac{12}{36}$$

A $\frac{4}{9}$

B $\frac{4}{12}$

C $\frac{1}{2}$

D $\frac{3}{9}$

6. What is the fraction $\frac{27}{72}$ in simplest form?

A $\frac{3}{4}$

B $\frac{3}{8}$

C $\frac{1}{9}$

D $\frac{4}{9}$

7. What is the greatest common factor (GCF) of 6 and 18?

A 1

B 3

C 6

D 18

8. The factors 1, 2, and 4 are common factors of which numbers?

A 4, 8, and 22

B 3, 6, and 9

C 4, 12, and 16

D 18, 27, and 36

9. A student survey shows that 8 out of 32 students in the class said they would go to summer camp this year. What fractional part of the class will go to summer camp?

A $\frac{1}{4}$

B $\frac{2}{3}$

C $\frac{2}{6}$

D $\frac{4}{11}$

Read the questions. Use the strategies to choose the answer choice that makes the most sense.

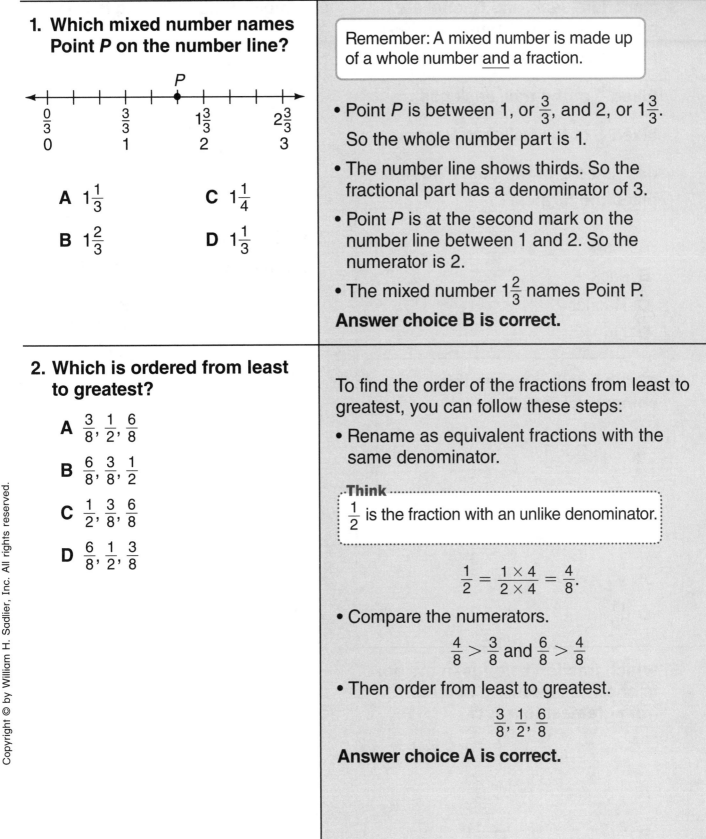

1. Which mixed number names Point _P_ on the number line?

A $1\frac{1}{3}$ C $1\frac{1}{4}$

B $1\frac{2}{3}$ D $1\frac{1}{3}$

Remember: A mixed number is made up of a whole number <u>and</u> a fraction.

- Point _P_ is between 1, or $\frac{3}{3}$, and 2, or $1\frac{3}{3}$. So the whole number part is 1.
- The number line shows thirds. So the fractional part has a denominator of 3.
- Point _P_ is at the second mark on the number line between 1 and 2. So the numerator is 2.
- The mixed number $1\frac{2}{3}$ names Point P.

Answer choice B is correct.

2. Which is ordered from least to greatest?

A $\frac{3}{8}, \frac{1}{2}, \frac{6}{8}$

B $\frac{6}{8}, \frac{3}{8}, \frac{1}{2}$

C $\frac{1}{2}, \frac{3}{8}, \frac{6}{8}$

D $\frac{6}{8}, \frac{1}{2}, \frac{3}{8}$

To find the order of the fractions from least to greatest, you can follow these steps:

- Rename as equivalent fractions with the same denominator.

Think
$\frac{1}{2}$ is the fraction with an unlike denominator.

$$\frac{1}{2} = \frac{1 \times 4}{2 \times 4} = \frac{4}{8}.$$

- Compare the numerators.

$$\frac{4}{8} > \frac{3}{8} \text{ and } \frac{6}{8} > \frac{4}{8}$$

- Then order from least to greatest.

$$\frac{3}{8}, \frac{1}{2}, \frac{6}{8}$$

Answer choice A is correct.

Name _____

Circle the letter of the correct answer choice.

3. Mark, Lin, Jack, and Rachel are hiking the same 3-mile trail. Mark has hiked $\frac{3}{4}$ of the trail. Lin has hiked $\frac{5}{8}$ of the trail, Jack has hiked $\frac{7}{8}$ of the trail, and Rachel has hiked $\frac{3}{8}$ of the trail. Who has hiked the farthest?

  A Mark

  B Jack

  C Rachel

  D Lin

4. Which fraction makes this comparison true?

$$\frac{3}{4} = \square$$

  A $\frac{12}{15}$

  B $\frac{15}{24}$

  C $\frac{6}{9}$

  D $\frac{15}{20}$

5. Which fraction belongs in the box to show the fractions in order from greatest to least?

$$\frac{7}{8}, \frac{5}{8}, \square, \frac{1}{4}$$

  A $\frac{1}{8}$ **C** $\frac{1}{2}$

  B $\frac{3}{4}$ **D** $\frac{14}{16}$

6. Which of the following is true?

  A $\frac{5}{6} < \frac{7}{12}$

  B $\frac{3}{4} < \frac{1}{2}$

  C $\frac{5}{12} > \frac{8}{12}$

  D $\frac{4}{8} = \frac{12}{24}$

7. Which point on the number line shows the mixed number $3\frac{2}{5}$?

  A M

  B O

  C N

  D P

8. Which fraction makes the comparison true?

$$\frac{4}{5} < \square$$

  A $\frac{9}{10}$

  B $\frac{3}{10}$

  C $\frac{12}{15}$

  D $\frac{18}{25}$

Read the questions. Use the strategies to choose the answer choice that makes the most sense.

STRATEGIES

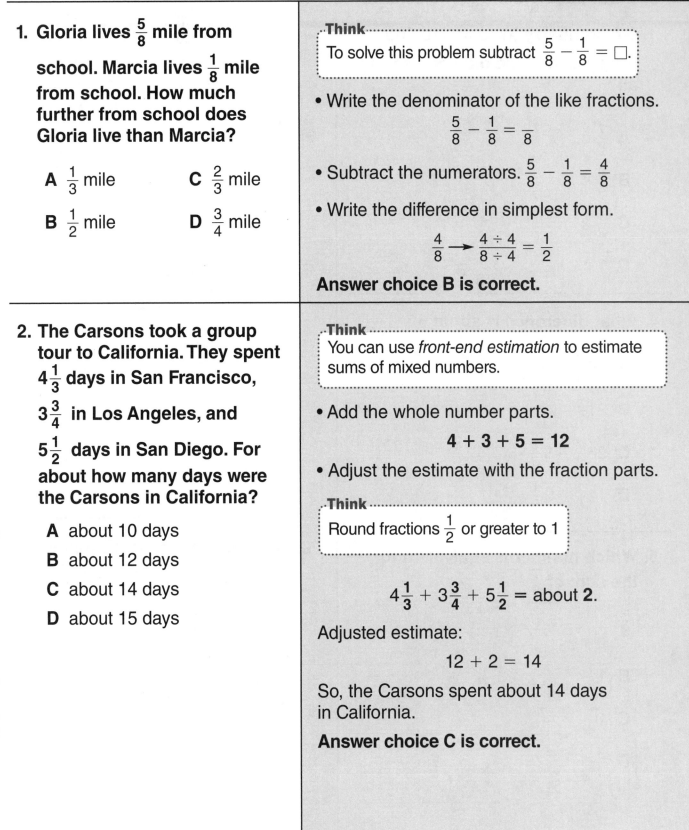

1. Gloria lives $\frac{5}{8}$ mile from school. Marcia lives $\frac{1}{8}$ mile from school. How much further from school does Gloria live than Marcia?

   A $\frac{1}{3}$ mile   **C** $\frac{2}{3}$ mile

   B $\frac{1}{2}$ mile   **D** $\frac{3}{4}$ mile

Think

To solve this problem subtract $\frac{5}{8} - \frac{1}{8} = \square$.

• Write the denominator of the like fractions.
$$\frac{5}{8} - \frac{1}{8} = \frac{\ }{8}$$

• Subtract the numerators. $\frac{5}{8} - \frac{1}{8} = \frac{4}{8}$

• Write the difference in simplest form.

$$\frac{4}{8} \longrightarrow \frac{4 \div 4}{8 \div 4} = \frac{1}{2}$$

Answer choice B is correct.

2. The Carsons took a group tour to California. They spent $4\frac{1}{3}$ days in San Francisco, $3\frac{3}{4}$ in Los Angeles, and $5\frac{1}{2}$ days in San Diego. For about how many days were the Carsons in California?

   A about 10 days

   B about 12 days

   C about 14 days

   D about 15 days

Think

You can use *front-end estimation* to estimate sums of mixed numbers.

• Add the whole number parts.
$$4 + 3 + 5 = 12$$

• Adjust the estimate with the fraction parts.

Think

Round fractions $\frac{1}{2}$ or greater to 1

$$4\frac{1}{3} + 3\frac{3}{4} + 5\frac{1}{2} = \text{about } \mathbf{2}.$$

Adjusted estimate:

$$12 + 2 = 14$$

So, the Carsons spent about 14 days in California.

Answer choice C is correct.

Circle the letter of the correct answer choice.

3. Carol used $\frac{1}{3}$ c orange juice and $\frac{2}{3}$ c cranberry juice in a recipe. How much liquid did she use in all?

   A $\frac{7}{8}$ c

   B $\frac{3}{4}$ c

   C $\frac{1}{2}$ c

   D 1 c

4. What difference is about 5?

   A $15\frac{3}{4} - 11\frac{1}{2}$

   B $21\frac{1}{2} - 15\frac{1}{4}$

   C $26\frac{7}{8} - 5\frac{1}{6}$

   D $14\frac{1}{5} - 9\frac{1}{6}$

5. Which number is equivalent to the sum of $\frac{7}{8} + \frac{5}{8}$?

   A $\frac{1}{2}$

   B $1\frac{1}{8}$

   C $1\frac{1}{2}$

   D $\frac{3}{2}$

6. Find the sum.

   $$\frac{1}{10} + \frac{3}{10}$$

   A $\frac{1}{2}$

   B $\frac{4}{20}$

   C $\frac{2}{5}$

   D $\frac{1}{5}$

7. Find the difference.

   $$\frac{7}{8} - \frac{3}{8}$$

   A $8\frac{1}{4}$

   B 4

   C $\frac{1}{2}$

   D $\frac{3}{4}$

8. What is a reasonable estimate for the sum of $31\frac{1}{2} + 9\frac{1}{4} + 24\frac{3}{8}$?

   A about 25

   B about 65

   C about 85

   D about 90

Read the questions. Use the strategies to choose the answer choice that makes the most sense.

STRATEGIES

1. **What is the least common multiple of 6, 8, and 12?**

   A 12

   B 24

   C 26

   D 576

Remember:
- The **multiples** of a number are all the *products* that have that number as a factor.
- The **least common multiple** (LCM) of two or more numbers is the *least* number that is a multiple of those numbers.

- List the multiples of each number.

  Multiples of 8: 8, 16, **24**, 32, . . .

  Multiples of 6: 6, 12, 18, **24**, 30, . . .

  Multiples of 12: 12, **24**, 36, 48, . . .

The least common multiple **(LCM)** of 8, 6, and 12 is 24.

Answer choice B is correct.

2. **Pedro made a casserole containing $\frac{1}{4}$ c mushrooms and $\frac{2}{3}$ c onions. How much more of his casserole contains onions than mushrooms?**

   A $\frac{1}{12}$

   B $\frac{1}{7}$

   C $\frac{5}{12}$

   D $\frac{11}{12}$

To solve the problem, subtract $\frac{1}{4}$ from $\frac{2}{3}$.

Think
These fractions have *unlike* denominators. You need to find the LCM of the two fractions.

LCM of 4 and 3 is **12**.
- Use the LCM to rename $\frac{1}{4}$ and $\frac{2}{3}$ as fractions with *like* denominators.

$$\frac{1}{4} = \frac{3}{12} \qquad \frac{2}{3} = \frac{8}{12}$$

- Subtract the like fractions.

$$\frac{8}{12} - \frac{3}{12} = \frac{5}{12}$$

So, onions make up $\frac{5}{12}$ more of the casserole.

Answer choice C is correct.

Name _____

Circle the letter of the correct answer choice.

3. **What is the least common multiple (LCM) of 4, 5, and 8?**

   A 8

   B 20

   C 40

   D 50

4. **Find the sum.**

$$\frac{5}{6} + \frac{2}{3}$$

   A $1\frac{1}{2}$

   B $\frac{7}{9}$

   C $\frac{1}{2}$

   D 1

5. **Which two fractions in the box have a difference of $\frac{3}{10}$?**

$$\boxed{\ \frac{1}{3} \quad \frac{3}{5} \quad \frac{1}{5} \quad \frac{9}{10} \quad \frac{4}{5}\ }$$

   A $\frac{1}{5}$ and $\frac{4}{5}$

   B $\frac{9}{10}$ and $\frac{1}{3}$

   C $\frac{3}{5}$ and $\frac{1}{5}$

   D $\frac{9}{10}$ and $\frac{3}{5}$

6. **Which answer choice has a sum of $\frac{3}{4}$?**

   A $\frac{1}{4} + \frac{3}{8}$

   B $\frac{7}{8} + \frac{1}{4}$

   C $\frac{3}{8} + \frac{3}{8}$

   D $\frac{11}{12} + \frac{3}{8}$

7. **How far is it from the bridge to the barn?**

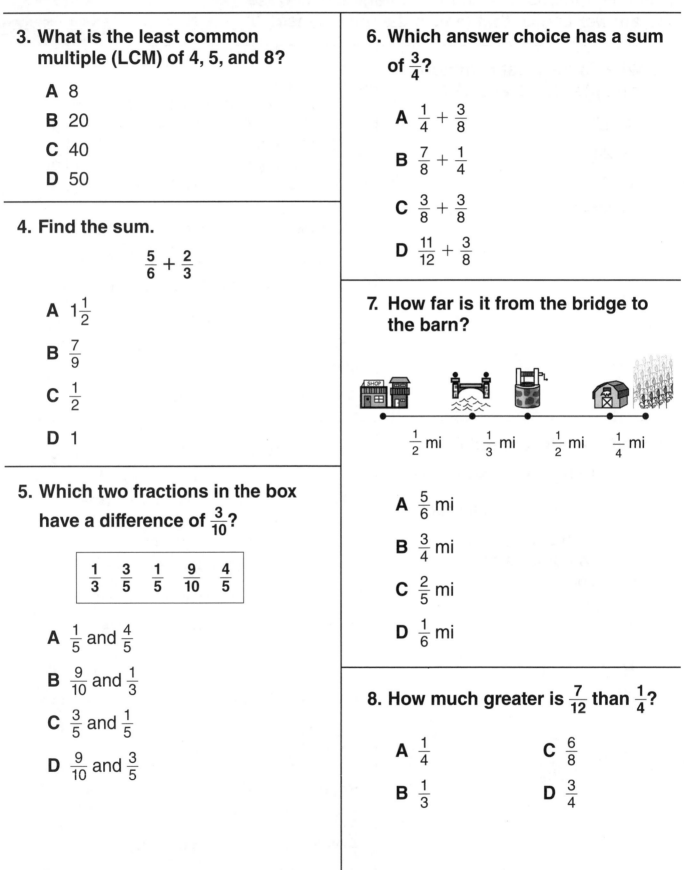

$\frac{1}{2}$ mi $\frac{1}{3}$ mi $\frac{1}{2}$ mi $\frac{1}{4}$ mi

   A $\frac{5}{6}$ mi

   B $\frac{3}{4}$ mi

   C $\frac{2}{5}$ mi

   D $\frac{1}{6}$ mi

8. **How much greater is $\frac{7}{12}$ than $\frac{1}{4}$?**

   A $\frac{1}{4}$ C $\frac{6}{8}$

   B $\frac{1}{3}$ D $\frac{3}{4}$

Read the questions. Use the strategies to choose the answer choice that makes the most sense.

STRATEGIES

1. **Harry tosses a number cube with the numbers 1 to 6. What is the probability that he tosses an *odd* number?**

   A $\frac{5}{6}$ **C** $\frac{1}{2}$

   B $\frac{3}{5}$ **D** $\frac{2}{3}$

   Think

   You can use fractions to find the probability of an event.

   - List the possible outcomes.

     1, 2, 3, 4, 5, and 6

   - List the favorable outcomes.

     odd numbers: 1, 3, and 5.

   - Find the probability.

   $P = \dfrac{\text{number of favorable outcomes}}{\text{number of possible outcomes}} = \dfrac{3}{6} = \dfrac{1}{2}$

   The probability that Harry tosses an odd number is $\frac{1}{2}$.

   Answer choice C is correct.

2. **Find the value of the variable.**

   $$\frac{2}{3} \text{ of } 18 = n$$

   A 6

   B 8

   C 10

   D 12

   To find a fractional part of a number, follow these steps:

   - Divide the whole number by the denominator.

   $\frac{2}{3}$ of 18 = n

        whole number

   denominator

   $18 \div 3 = 6$

       quotient

   - Multiply the quotient by the numerator.

   $$6 \quad \times \quad 2 = \textbf{12}$$

   quotient   numerator

   So, $\frac{2}{3}$ of 18 = 12.

   Answer choice D is correct.

Name _____

Circle the letter of the correct answer choice.

3. You reach into a bag that has 6 red marbles, 4 yellow marbles, 2 green marbles, and 3 white marbles. You reach in without looking and pick a marble. What is the probability you will pick a yellow marble?

   A $\frac{1}{4}$

   B $\frac{4}{11}$

   C $\frac{4}{15}$

   D $\frac{11}{15}$

4. Betty tosses a number cube with numbers 1 to 6. What is the probability she will toss a number less than 7?

   A $\frac{1}{6}$ C $\frac{1}{7}$

   B $\frac{2}{3}$ D 1

5. There are 32 students in Claudia's class. Five eighths of them are girls. How many girls are in the class?

   A 24

   B 20

   C 8

   D 5

6. If the spinner below is spun once, what is the probability of landing on a 2?

   A $\frac{1}{4}$

   B $\frac{6}{21}$

   C $\frac{3}{8}$

   D 3

7. Find the value of the variable.

   $$\frac{5}{6} \text{ of } 54 = s$$

   A 9

   B 10

   C 18

   D 45

8. Which is true?

   A Five sixths of 30 is y. $y = 5$

   B Three fifths of 35 is n. $n = 21$

   C Two thirds of 48 is m. $m = 36$

   D Seven eighths of 40 is r. $r = 32$

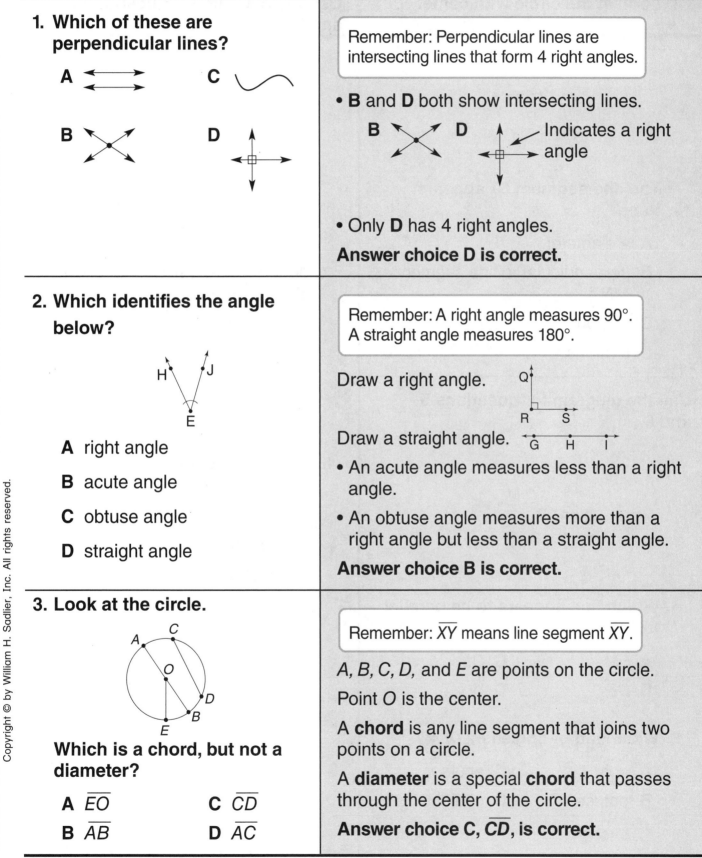

Read the questions. Use the strategies to choose the answer choice that makes the most sense.

STRATEGIES

1. Which of these are perpendicular lines?

A   B   C   D

Remember: Perpendicular lines are intersecting lines that form 4 right angles.

• **B** and **D** both show intersecting lines.

B   D — Indicates a right angle

• Only **D** has 4 right angles.

Answer choice D is correct.

2. Which identifies the angle below?

A right angle

B acute angle

C obtuse angle

D straight angle

Remember: A right angle measures 90°. A straight angle measures 180°.

Draw a right angle.

Draw a straight angle.

• An acute angle measures less than a right angle.

• An obtuse angle measures more than a right angle but less than a straight angle.

Answer choice B is correct.

3. Look at the circle.

Which is a chord, but not a diameter?

A $\overline{EO}$ **C** $\overline{CD}$

B $\overline{AB}$ **D** $\overline{AC}$

Remember: $\overline{XY}$ means line segment $\overline{XY}$.

A, B, C, D, and *E* are points on the circle.

Point *O* is the center.

A **chord** is any line segment that joins two points on a circle.

A **diameter** is a special **chord** that passes through the center of the circle.

Answer choice C, $\overline{CD}$, is correct.

Name _____

Circle the letter of the correct answer choice.

4. Look at the circle with center *S*.

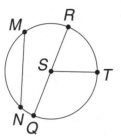

The line segment *ST* appears to be

A a diameter.

B perpendicular to line segment *MN*.

C a chord.

D a radius.

Use the diagram for questions 5 and 6.

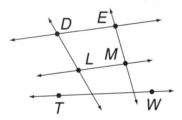

5. Which line appears to be parallel to $\overleftrightarrow{LM}$?

A $\overleftrightarrow{EM}$ **C** $\overrightarrow{DL}$

B $\overleftrightarrow{DE}$ **D** $\overleftrightarrow{WT}$

6. What kind of angle is ∠*DLM*?

A right   **C** acute

B obtuse   **D** straight

Use the diagram for questions 7 and 8.

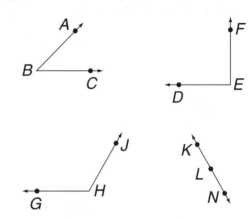

7. Which angle appears to be an obtuse angle?

A ∠*ABC*

B ∠*DEF*

C ∠*GHJ*

D ∠*KLN*

8. Which angle appears to be an acute angle?

A ∠*ABC*

B ∠*DEF*

C ∠*GHJ*

D ∠*KLN*

Read the questions. Use the strategies to choose the answer choice that makes the most sense.

STRATEGIES

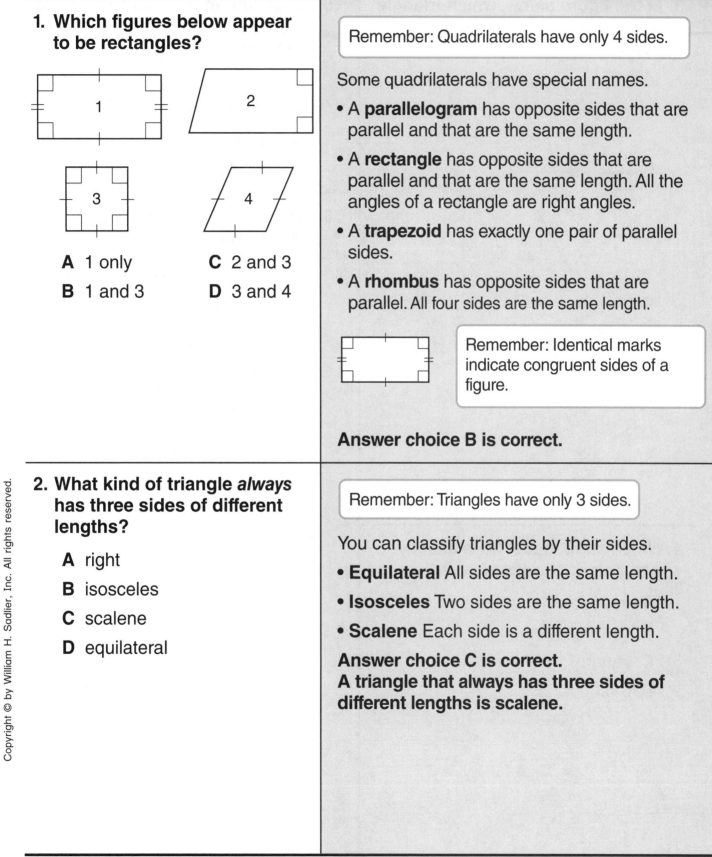

1. Which figures below appear to be rectangles?

A 1 only   **C** 2 and 3

B 1 and 3   **D** 3 and 4

Remember: Quadrilaterals have only 4 sides.

Some quadrilaterals have special names.

• A **parallelogram** has opposite sides that are parallel and that are the same length.

• A **rectangle** has opposite sides that are parallel and that are the same length. All the angles of a rectangle are right angles.

• A **trapezoid** has exactly one pair of parallel sides.

• A **rhombus** has opposite sides that are parallel. All four sides are the same length.

Remember: Identical marks indicate congruent sides of a figure.

Answer choice B is correct.

2. What kind of triangle *always* has three sides of different lengths?

A right

B isosceles

C scalene

D equilateral

Remember: Triangles have only 3 sides.

You can classify triangles by their sides.

• **Equilateral** All sides are the same length.

• **Isosceles** Two sides are the same length.

• **Scalene** Each side is a different length.

Answer choice C is correct.
A triangle that always has three sides of different lengths is scalene.

Circle the letter of the correct answer choice.

3. **In the figure below, which triangle appears to be an equilateral triangle?**

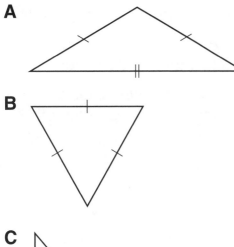

4. **Which shape must have exactly one pair of parallel sides?**

   A trapezoid

   B rectangle

   C square

   D rhombus

5. **What kind of triangle always has one right angle and two sides the same length?**

   A acute

   B right scalene

   C right isosceles

   D equilateral

6. **Which pair of figures appear to be similar?**

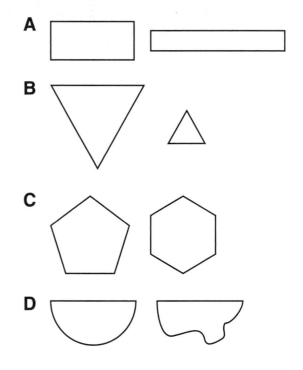

Read the questions. Use the strategies to choose the answer choice that makes the most sense.

STRATEGIES

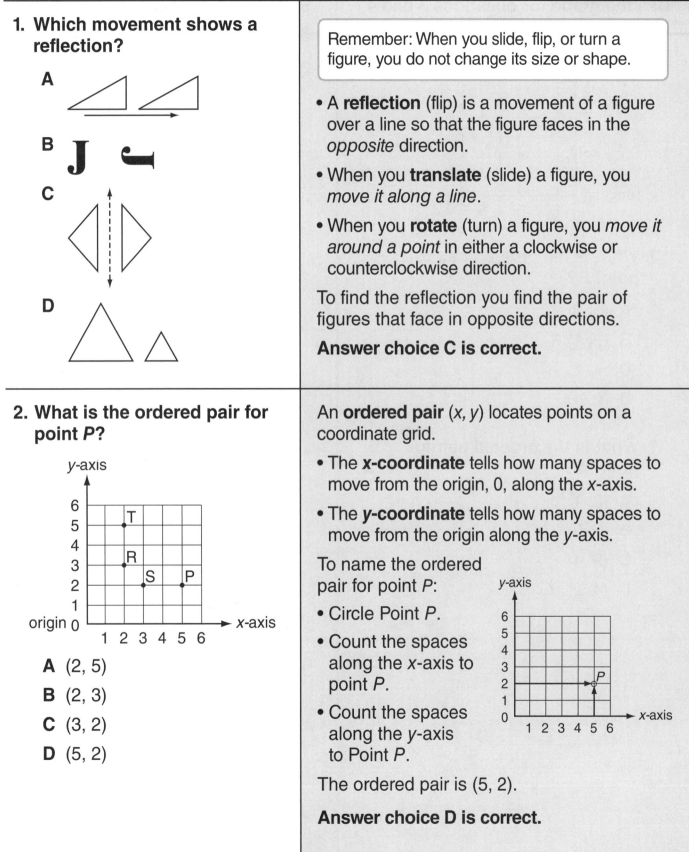

1. Which movement shows a reflection?

A

B **J ͻ**

C

D

Remember: When you slide, flip, or turn a figure, you do not change its size or shape.

- A **reflection** (flip) is a movement of a figure over a line so that the figure faces in the *opposite* direction.

- When you **translate** (slide) a figure, you *move it along a line*.

- When you **rotate** (turn) a figure, you *move it around a point* in either a clockwise or counterclockwise direction.

To find the reflection you find the pair of figures that face in opposite directions.

Answer choice C is correct.

2. What is the ordered pair for point *P*?

y-axis

origin 0 → *x*-axis

A (2, 5)

B (2, 3)

C (3, 2)

D (5, 2)

An **ordered pair** (*x*, *y*) locates points on a coordinate grid.

- The **x-coordinate** tells how many spaces to move from the origin, 0, along the *x*-axis.

- The **y-coordinate** tells how many spaces to move from the origin along the *y*-axis.

To name the ordered pair for point *P*:

- Circle Point *P*.

- Count the spaces along the *x*-axis to point *P*.

- Count the spaces along the *y*-axis to Point *P*.

y-axis

x-axis

The ordered pair is (5, 2).

Answer choice D is correct.

Name _____

Circle the letter of the correct answer choice.

Use the graph for questions 3 and 4.

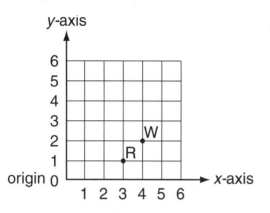

3. What is the ordered pair for point *R*?

   A (1, 3)

   B (3, 1)

   C (4, 2)

   D (2, 4)

4. What is the ordered pair for point *W*?

   A (3, 1)

   B (2, 2)

   C (2, 4)

   D (4, 2)

5. Which movement shows a turn?

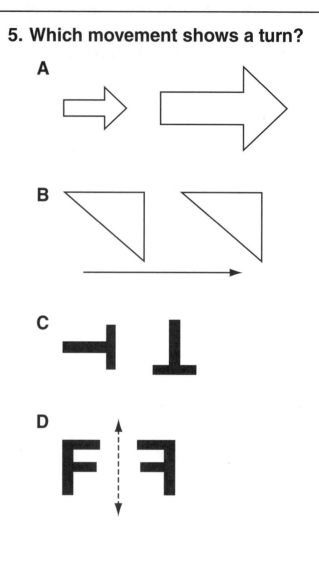

Read the problem. Use the Problem-Solving Guide below to help you think about the answer choices.

Seventy-two 4th graders are in after-school clubs. One fourth are in the Chess Club and three eighths are in the Math Club. These two clubs merge into a Math Knights Club. How many of the seventy-two 4th graders are Math Knights?

A $\frac{5}{8}$

C 27

B 45

D 14

PROBLEM-SOLVING GUIDE

① Understand the Question

- The question is asking you to find how many 4th graders belong to the Math Knights.
- You need to find part of 72.
- There is more than one-step.

② Understand Word Meanings

Merge means "join together."

Knight is the name of a chess piece. Math Knights is a good name for people interested in chess and in math.

③ Understand How to Solve

- First, add $\frac{1}{4}$ and $\frac{3}{8}$ to find the fraction of students that are Math Knights.

- Use the least common multiple to rename $\frac{1}{4}$ and $\frac{3}{8}$.

  Multiples of 4: 4, 8, 12 . . . Multiples of 8: 8, 16 . . . Least Common Multiple: 8

$$\frac{1}{4} = \frac{2}{8} \qquad \frac{3}{8} = \frac{3}{8} \qquad \frac{2}{8} + \frac{3}{8} = \frac{5}{8}$$

- Then find $\frac{5}{8}$ of 72.

Think

To find a fractional part of a number, divide by the denominator, then multiply the quotient by the numerator.

$$\frac{5}{8} \text{ of } 72 : 72 \div 8 = 9 \longrightarrow 9 \times 5 = 45$$

④ Circle the Letter of the Correct Answer Choice.

Answer choice B is correct.
45 of the 72 fourth-graders belong to the Math Knights.

Name _____

Circle the letter of the correct answer choice.

Mr. Maxwell builds a skating rink in the shape of a trapezoid. He says, "This rink has a unique shape." What is unique about the shape of a trapezoid compared to other quadrilaterals?

    A It has opposite sides that are the same length.

    B It has opposite sides that are parallel and the same length.

    C It has exactly one pair of parallel sides.

    D It has opposite sides that are parallel.

Complete each sentence.

❶ Understand the Question

• You must compare the shape of a _____ to other _____.

❷ Understand Word Meanings: unique

• My dog is **unique** because it is different from other dogs.

• Write your own definition of **_unique_** _____

_____

_____.

❸ Understand How to Solve

• Draw a trapezoid and extend the sides.

• The dotted lines show that two of the sides will never intersect. Lines on a flat plane that never intersect are parallel.

• A trapezoid has exactly one pair of sides that are parallel.

❹ Circle the Letter of the Correct Answer Choice.

Answer choice C is correct. A trapezoid is different from other quadrilaterals because it has exactly one pair of parallel sides.

Name _____

Circle the letter of the correct answer choice.

1. Ted painted a sign. He painted $\frac{5}{8}$ of its letters blue. Which shows this fraction in words?

   A eight fifths

   B three fifths

   C five eighths

   D eight thirds

2. The sketch below shows how much of a farmer's field is planted with wheat. About what fraction of the field is planted with wheat?

   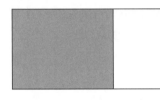

   A about nine tenths

   B about two thirds

   C about two fifths

   D about one fourth

3. The band played 15 songs at the concert. Five of the songs were on their CD. What fractional part of the songs were on the CD?

   A $\frac{1}{5}$ C $\frac{2}{3}$

   B $\frac{1}{3}$ D $\frac{15}{20}$

4. An ant crawled along the floor. It went $\frac{2}{3}$ ft in one direction, $\frac{1}{6}$ ft in another direction, and then $\frac{2}{3}$ ft in a third direction. How far did it crawl altogether?

   A 2 ft

   B 1 ft 6 in.

   C 1 ft 3 in.

   D 9 in.

5. The post office is $\frac{7}{8}$ mi from the bank, $\frac{1}{4}$ mi from the library, $\frac{1}{2}$ mi from the bakery, and $\frac{3}{4}$ mi from the school. Which is the farthest from the post office?

   A library   C bank

   B school   D bakery

6. You draw a triangle with a right angle. Two sides are the same length. Which shows two ways you could name the triangle?

   A right; isosceles

   B right; scalene

   C obtuse; isosceles

   D acute; scalene

7. A spinner has four sections, all the same size. Two sections are blue, one is red, and one is green. You spin the spinner. What is the probability of the spinner landing on red or green?

A 1

B $\frac{2}{4}$

C $\frac{1}{4}$

D 0

8. Mike used seven eighths of a yard of fabric to make a scarf. Reggie used one fourth of a yard less than Mike did. How much fabric did Reggie use?

A $\frac{3}{4}$ yd

B $\frac{5}{8}$ yd

C $\frac{3}{8}$ yd

D $\frac{1}{4}$ yd

9. Ike walked three fourths of the trail in the morning and the rest in the afternoon. If the trail is 12 miles long, how far did Ike walk in the afternoon?

A 12 mi   **C** 3 mi

B 9 mi   **D** $\frac{1}{4}$ mi

10. Alex cuts a loaf of banana bread into 8 equal parts. He gives away $\frac{1}{4}$ of the loaf. Which fraction names the same part of the loaf as $\frac{1}{4}$?

A $\frac{1}{2}$

B $\frac{1}{8}$

C $\frac{2}{8}$

D $\frac{4}{8}$

11. Abby cuts an orange into 6 equal parts. She gives $\frac{2}{3}$ of the orange to Jacob. How much of the orange does Abby keep?

A $\frac{2}{3}$

B $\frac{6}{9}$

C $\frac{1}{6}$

D $\frac{2}{6}$

12. You roll a number cube with faces 1, 3, 5, 7, 9, and 11. What is the probability that you will roll an even number?

A 0

B $\frac{1}{6}$

C $\frac{1}{2}$

D 1

Circle the letter of the correct answer choice.

13. The drawing shows the border of a rock garden that Paul designed. Which figure best describes the shape?

A equilateral triangle

B scalene triangle

C right triangle

D obtuse triangle

14. Ray drew a sketch showing the paths that cross the circular green in his village. Which path is a radius of the circle?

A Beech Walk

B Fir Walk

C Spruce Lane

D Pine Path

15. The drawing shows the intersection of four roads in Pilar's neighborhood. Which statement about the roads appears to be true?

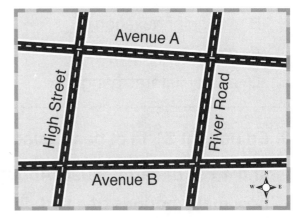

A River Road is perpendicular to High Street.

B Avenue A is parallel to Avenue B.

C Avenue B is perpendicular to River Road

D High Street is parallel to River Road.

16. Nita drew the following figure. What did she draw?

B ←●━━━━━━━━━●→ *A*

A a plane

B a ray

C a line segment

D a point

17. Parker posed the following riddle:

I am a 5-sided polygon. All my sides are the same length. All my angles have the same measure. What figure am I?

What is the figure?

  A an octagon

  B a regular hexagon

  C a regular pentagon

  D an equilateral triangle

---

18. Ed bought $2\frac{3}{4}$ lb of bean salad and $4\frac{1}{8}$ lb of carrot salad. About how many pounds of salad did Ed buy altogether?

  A about 1 lb

  B about 6 lb

  C about 7 lb

  D about 8 lb

---

19. A path meets the sidewalk near Nora's house at an angle of 120°. What can you say about the angle formed by the path and sidewalk?

  A It is acute.

  B It is right.

  C It is obtuse.

  D It is straight.

---

20. It took Colleen $\frac{1}{3}$ h to finish a puzzle. It took Lucia $\frac{5}{6}$ h to finish. How much longer did it take Lucia to finish the puzzle?

  A one half hour

  B one sixth hour

  C two thirds hour

  D one and one sixth hours

---

21. Juan found the old treasure map shown below. A note written on the back of the map says that the treasure is hidden at point (4, 3). Which letter names the location of the treasure?

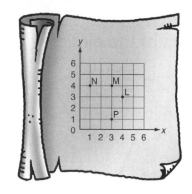

  A L

  B M

  C N

  D P

Name _____

Circle the letter of the correct answer.

1. Jo made a bar graph that shows how many of each geometric figure is in the picture below.

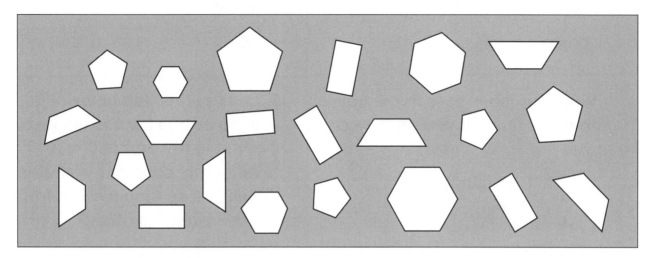

Which of the following bar graphs did Jo make?

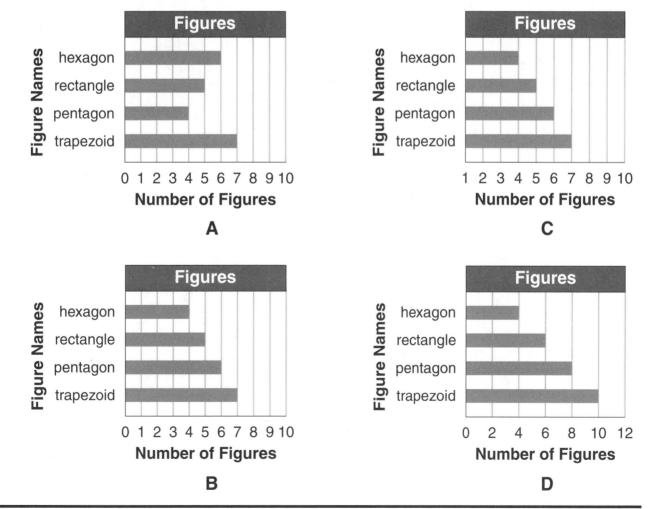

2. Which shows the solution for this number sentence?

$$3(2c + xqt) = 18c$$

A $3(2c + 4qt) = 18c$

B $(3 \times 2c) + (3 \times 4c) = 18c$

C $(3 \times 2c) + 4c = 18c$

D $3(2c + 12c) = 18c$

3. Which number goes in the box to make this number sentence true?

$$\frac{1}{4} h + 10 \text{ min} = \frac{3}{4} h - \square$$

A $\frac{1}{2} h$　　　　**C** $\frac{1}{4} h$

B 15 min　　　　**D** 20 min

4. Which point on the coordinate grid has a product of 12 with its second coordinate equal to one-third of its first coordinate?

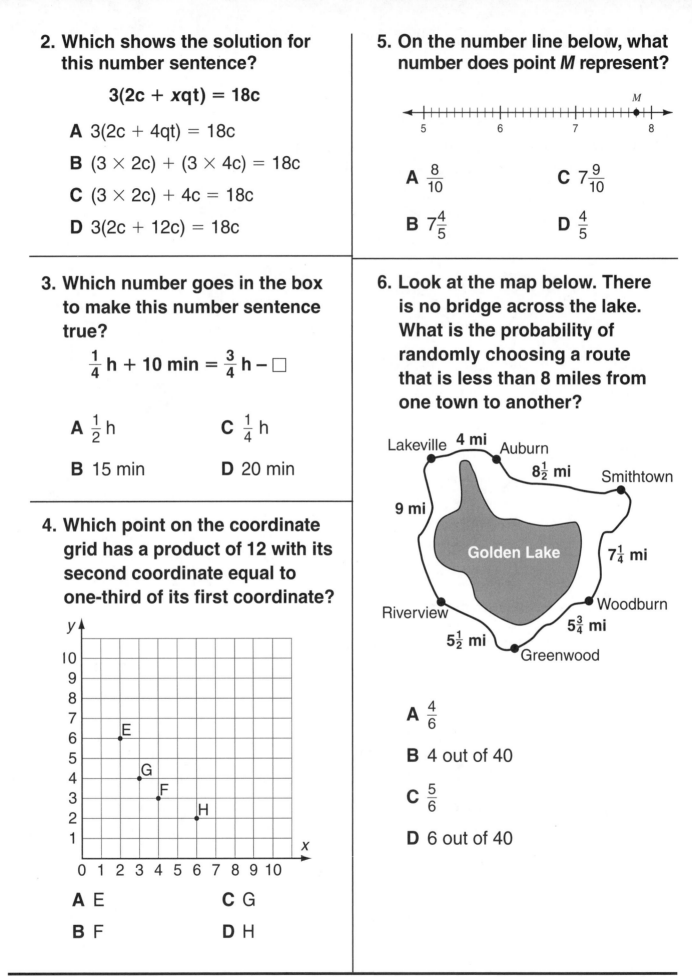

A E　　　　**C** G

B F　　　　**D** H

5. On the number line below, what number does point *M* represent?

A $\frac{8}{10}$　　　　**C** $7\frac{9}{10}$

B $7\frac{4}{5}$　　　　**D** $\frac{4}{5}$

6. Look at the map below. There is no bridge across the lake. What is the probability of randomly choosing a route that is less than 8 miles from one town to another?

Lakeville　4 mi　Auburn

$8\frac{1}{2}$ mi　Smithtown

9 mi

Golden Lake　$7\frac{1}{4}$ mi

Riverview　Woodburn

$5\frac{1}{2}$ mi　$5\frac{3}{4}$ mi

Greenwood

A $\frac{4}{6}$

B 4 out of 40

C $\frac{5}{6}$

D 6 out of 40

Read the questions. Use the strategies to choose
the answer choice that makes the most sense.

STRATEGIES

---

1. **What is the perimeter of the figure below?**

14 m

7 m

A 98 m   **C** 42 m

B 56 m   **D** 21 m

Think
Perimeter is the distance around a figure. The figure is a rectangle. You can use a formula to find the perimeter of a rectangle.

• To find the perimeter of a rectangle, use the formula:

perimeter   length   width

$$P = 2 \times \ell + 2 \times w$$
$$P = (2 \times \mathbf{14}) + (2 \times \mathbf{7})$$

Use $\ell = 14$ and $w = 7$.

$$P = \quad \mathbf{28} \quad + \quad \mathbf{14}$$
$$P = 42 \text{ m}$$

The perimeter of the rectangle is 42 m.

Answer choice C is correct.

---

2. **A squash court is a rectangle. It is 32 feet long and 21 feet wide. What is the area of a squash court?**

A 53 ft^2

B 106 ft^2

C 672 ft

D 672 ft^2

Think
Area is the number of **square units** needed to cover a flat surface. To find the area of the squash court, you can use the area formula for a rectangle.

• To find the area of a rectangle, use the formula $A = \ell \times w$.

• To find the area of the squash court:

$$A = \ell \times w$$
$$A = \mathbf{32} \times \mathbf{21}$$

Use $\ell = 32$ and $w = 21$.

$$A = 672 \text{ ft}^2$$

Answer choice **C** is *incorrect* because the answer is not given in square units.

Answer choice D is correct.

Name _____

Circle the letter of the correct answer choice.

3. A park is in the shape of an equilateral triangle. Each side is 150 yards long. What is the perimeter of the park?

 A 450 yd²

 B 450 yd

 C 150 yd

 D 50 yd

4. Which statement about the figures is true?

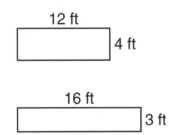

12 ft

4 ft

16 ft

3 ft

 A They both have the same perimeter.

 B They both have the same length.

 C They both have the same width.

 D They both have the same area.

5. Which will give the perimeter of a rectangle with a length of 12 feet and a width of 8 feet?

 A $P = (2 \times 12) + (2 \times 12)$

 B $P = 12 + 2 + 8$

 C $P = (2 + 12) + (2 + 8)$

 D $P = (2 \times 12) + (2 \times 8)$

Use the figure for questions 6 and 7.

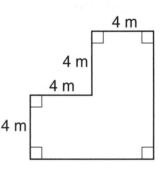

4 m

4 m

4 m

4 m

6. What is the perimeter of the figure?

 A 16 m

 B 24 m

 C 32 m

 D 32 m²

7. What is the area of the above figure?

 A 64 m²   C 24 m²

 B 48 m²   D 16 m²

8. A rectangle has a perimeter of 18 in. and an area of 18 in.². What are the measurements of its sides?

 A 9 in. and 2 in.

 B 8 in. and 1 in.

 C 6 in. and 3 in.

 D 12 in. and 6 in.

Read the questions. Use the strategies to choose the answer choice that makes the most sense.

STRATEGIES

1. **Which solid figure does the following net form when it is folded on the dotted lines without overlapping?**

   A rectangular prism
   B square pyramid
   C triangular prism
   D cylinder

   Think
   A **net** is a flat pattern that folds into a solid figure. This net has *five faces*: three rectangles and two triangles.

   • Look at the answer choices.

   A: A rectangular prism has 6 faces.

   D: A cylinder has 0 faces.

   • Eliminate answer choices **A** and **D**.

   Answer choice **B:** square pyramid and answer choice **C:** triangular prism, have five faces.

   • Only the triangular prism has *two faces* that are triangles and *three faces* that are rectangles.

   Answer choice C is correct.

2. **How many connecting cubes do you need to build this solid figure?**

   A 26   C 40
   B 30   D 45

   To find the number of cubes in the figure:

   • Count the layers: There are **3** layers.

   • Count the cubes in each layer.

   Think
   You cannot always see all cubes in each layer.

   Bottom layer: 5×5, or **25** cubes

   Middle layer: 4×4, or **16** cubes

   Top layer: 2×2, or **4** cubes

   • Add the cubes in the 3 layers:

   $$25 + 16 + 4 = 45$$

   Answer choice D is correct.

Name _____

Circle the letter of the correct answer choice.

3. A solid figure has 5 faces, 8 edges, and 5 vertices. Which figure is it?

   A cone

   B square pyramid

   C triangular prism

   D rectangular prism

4. Which solid figure does the following net form when it is folded on the dotted lines without overlapping?

   A rectangular prism

   B square pyramid

   C cube

   D cylinder

5. You build a rectangular prism with ℓ = 6 cubes, w = 3 cubes, and h = 4 cubes. How many cubes do you use in all?

   A 13   **C** 24

   B 18   **D** 72

6. Which figure is built with 36 connecting cubes?

   A

   B

   C

   D

7. How many edges does a triangular prism have?

   A 12

   B 9

   C 8

   D 0

Read the questions. Use the strategies to choose the answer choice that makes the most sense.

STRATEGIES

1. **Which figure has a volume of 480 cubic centimeters?**

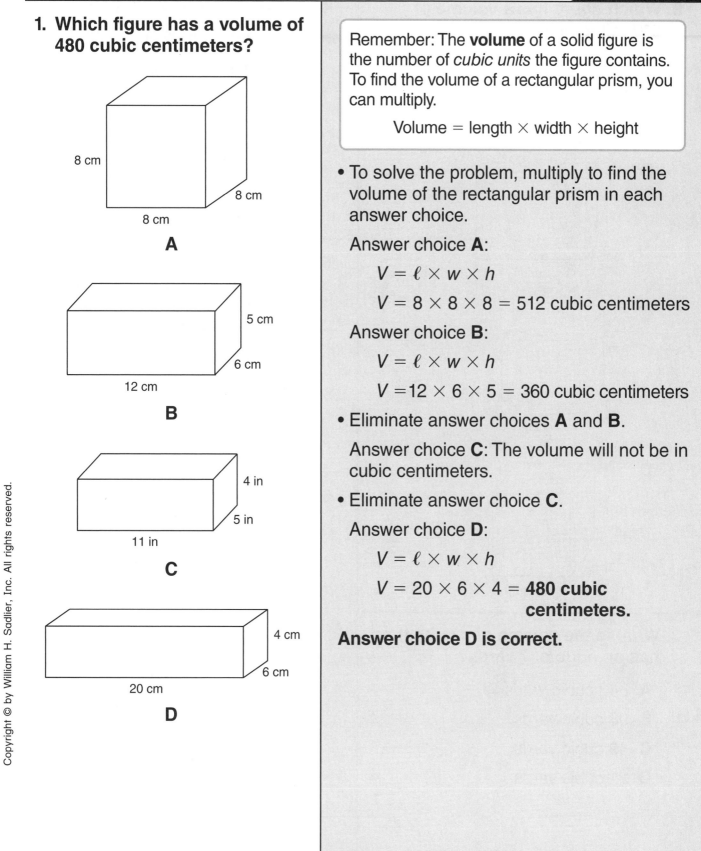

Remember: The **volume** of a solid figure is the number of *cubic units* the figure contains. To find the volume of a rectangular prism, you can multiply.

Volume = length × width × height

- To solve the problem, multiply to find the volume of the rectangular prism in each answer choice.

Answer choice **A**:

$V = \ell \times w \times h$

$V = 8 \times 8 \times 8 = 512$ cubic centimeters

Answer choice **B**:

$V = \ell \times w \times h$

$V = 12 \times 6 \times 5 = 360$ cubic centimeters

- Eliminate answer choices **A** and **B**.

Answer choice **C**: The volume will not be in cubic centimeters.

- Eliminate answer choice **C**.

Answer choice **D**:

$V = \ell \times w \times h$

$V = 20 \times 6 \times 4 =$ **480 cubic centimeters.**

Answer choice D is correct.

Name _____

Circle the letter of the correct answer choice.

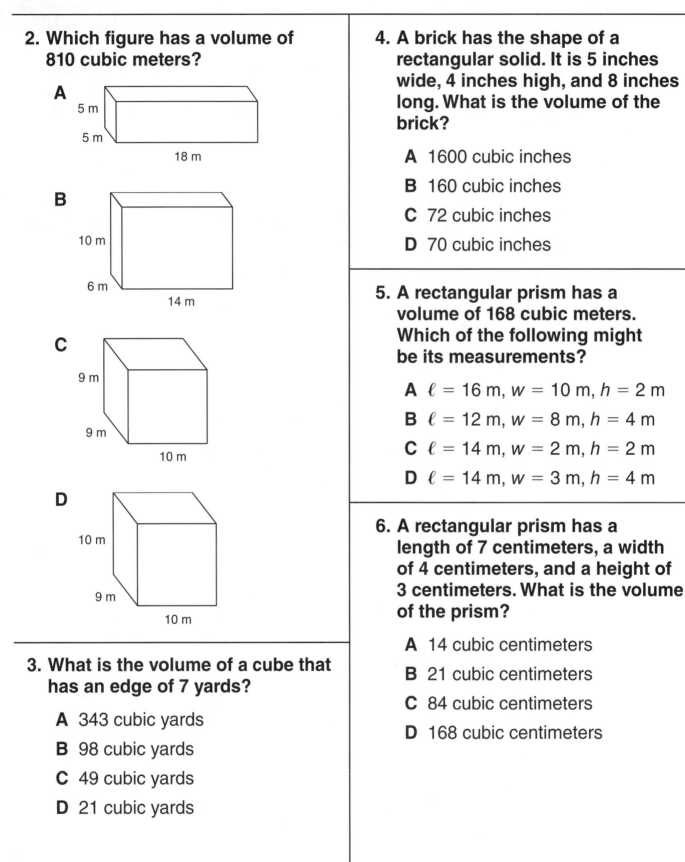

2. **Which figure has a volume of 810 cubic meters?**

A 5 m 5 m 18 m

B 10 m 6 m 14 m

C 9 m 9 m 10 m

D 10 m 9 m 10 m

3. **What is the volume of a cube that has an edge of 7 yards?**

A 343 cubic yards

B 98 cubic yards

C 49 cubic yards

D 21 cubic yards

4. **A brick has the shape of a rectangular solid. It is 5 inches wide, 4 inches high, and 8 inches long. What is the volume of the brick?**

A 1600 cubic inches

B 160 cubic inches

C 72 cubic inches

D 70 cubic inches

5. **A rectangular prism has a volume of 168 cubic meters. Which of the following might be its measurements?**

A $\ell = 16$ m, $w = 10$ m, $h = 2$ m

B $\ell = 12$ m, $w = 8$ m, $h = 4$ m

C $\ell = 14$ m, $w = 2$ m, $h = 2$ m

D $\ell = 14$ m, $w = 3$ m, $h = 4$ m

6. **A rectangular prism has a length of 7 centimeters, a width of 4 centimeters, and a height of 3 centimeters. What is the volume of the prism?**

A 14 cubic centimeters

B 21 cubic centimeters

C 84 cubic centimeters

D 168 cubic centimeters

Read the questions. Use the strategies to choose the answer choice that makes the most sense.

STRATEGIES

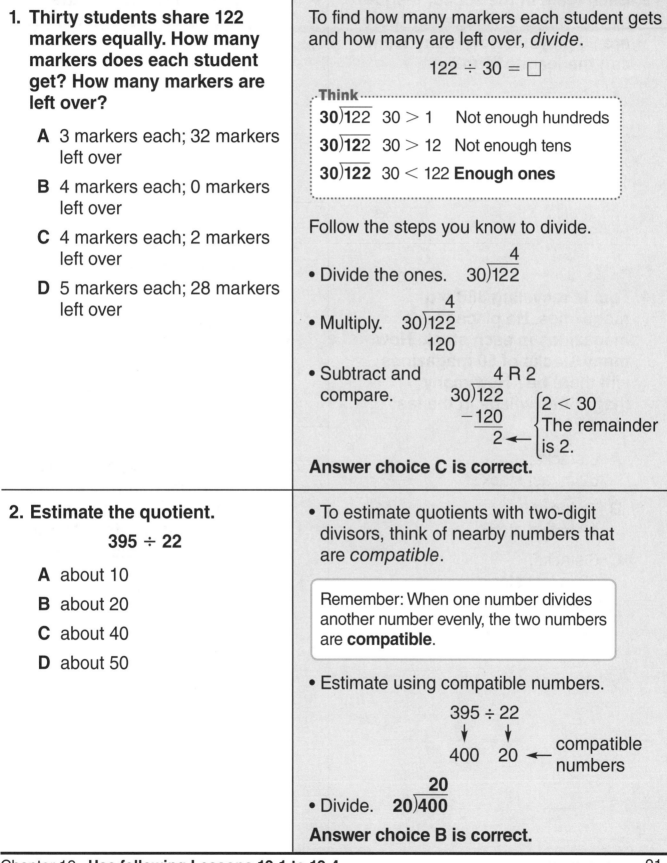

1. **Thirty students share 122 markers equally. How many markers does each student get? How many markers are left over?**

   A 3 markers each; 32 markers left over

   B 4 markers each; 0 markers left over

   C 4 markers each; 2 markers left over

   D 5 markers each; 28 markers left over

To find how many markers each student gets and how many are left over, *divide*.

$$122 \div 30 = \square$$

Think

$30\overline{)122}$ $30 > 1$ Not enough hundreds

$30\overline{)122}$ $30 > 12$ Not enough tens

$30\overline{)122}$ $30 < 122$ **Enough ones**

Follow the steps you know to divide.

- Divide the ones. $30\overline{)122}^{\,4}$

- Multiply. $\begin{array}{r} 4 \\ 30\overline{)122} \\ 120 \end{array}$

- Subtract and compare. $\begin{array}{r} 4\ R\ 2 \\ 30\overline{)122} \\ -120 \\ \hline 2 \end{array}$ $\begin{cases} 2 < 30 \\ \text{The remainder} \\ \text{is 2.} \end{cases}$

Answer choice C is correct.

2. **Estimate the quotient.**

   $$395 \div 22$$

   A about 10

   B about 20

   C about 40

   D about 50

- To estimate quotients with two-digit divisors, think of nearby numbers that are *compatible*.

Remember: When one number divides another number evenly, the two numbers are **compatible**.

- Estimate using compatible numbers.

  $\begin{array}{c} 395 \div 22 \\ \downarrow \quad\ \downarrow \\ 400 \quad 20 \end{array}$ ← compatible numbers

- Divide. $20\overline{)400}^{\,20}$

Answer choice B is correct.

Circle the letter of the correct answer choice.

3. Each team in the soccer league has 12 players. Altogether there are 96 players. How many teams can the league form?

   A 80

   B 12

   C 8

   D 7

4. Tom is recycling 338 old magazines. He places 50 magazines in each stack. How many stacks of 50 magazines will there be? How many magazines will be in the last stack?

   A 8 stacks;
      62 in last stack

   B 7 stacks;
      12 in last stack

   C 6 stacks;
      38 in last stack

   D 6 stacks;
      12 in last stack

5. The quotient is 700 and the dividend is 21,000. What is the divisor?

   A 3

   B 30

   C 300

   D 3000

6. Which is the most reasonable estimate of 5922 ÷ 23?

   A about 30

   B about 200

   C about 300

   D about 500

7. Ms. Rose's class spent a total of $91.48 for lunch during a class visit to the science museum. If there are 28 students in the class, about how much did each spend for lunch?

   A about $30

   B about $5

   C about $4

   D about $3

Read the questions. Use the strategies to choose the answer choice that makes the most sense.

1. **There are 254 people who want to take the tram tour through the animal park. How many trams with 52 passengers will there be? How many passengers will be on the last tram?**

   A 5 trips; 0 passengers

   B 5 trips; 4 passengers

   C 4 trips; 56 passengers

   D 4 trips; 46 passengers

To find how many trams are needed, you can divide $254 \div 52$.

- $52\overline{)254}$ $52 > 2; 52 > 25$

  Not enough hundreds or tens.

- $52\overline{)254}$ $52 < 254$

  Enough ones. Now you can divide.

> **Think**
> When the quotient you choose is too large, you need to change your **trial quotient**.

- Estimate. $25 \div 5 = 5$.
  Try 5 as the trial quotient.

$$\begin{array}{r} 5 \\ 52\overline{)254} \\ 260 \end{array}$$ $260 > 254$ Too large. Try 4.

- $$\begin{array}{r} 4 \text{ R } 46 \\ 52\overline{)254} \\ -208 \\ \hline 46 \end{array}$$

Answer choice D is correct.

2. **Find the quotient.**

   $$26\overline{)1316}$$

   A 45

   B 50

   C 50 R16

   D 60 R 15

> Remember: *Estimate* to place the first digit in the quotient.

- Try 4 as the first digit.

$$\begin{array}{r} 4 \\ 26\overline{)1316} \\ -104 \\ \hline 27 \end{array}$$

> **Think**
> $27 > 26$. The estimate is not enough. Adjust the estimate.

- Try 5 as the first digit.

$$\begin{array}{r} 50 \text{ R16} \\ 26\overline{)1316} \\ -130 \downarrow \\ \hline 16 \\ -0 \\ \hline 16 \end{array}$$

> **Think**
> $1 < 26$ The estimate is enough.

- Complete the division.

Answer choice C is correct.

Circle the letter of the correct answer choice.

3. Find the quotient.

$$54\overline{)3883}$$

  A 61 R4

  B 71

  C 71 R49

  D 75

4. A florist had 128 carnations. If she put 21 carnations in each vase, at most how many vases did she use? How many carnations were left over?

  A 6 vases; 2 carnations left over

  B 6 vases; 0 carnations left over

  C 5 vases; 23 carnations left over

  D 3 vases; 65 carnations left over

5. Carmen and her 30 classmates collected a total of 899 bottles for recycling. If each student collected the same number of bottles, which would be the most each could collect?

  A 28

  B 29

  C 30

  D 31

6. The quotient is 4 and the dividend is 248. What is the divisor?

  A 992

  B 62

  C 50

  D 6

7. Find the quotient.

$$\$5.52 \div 24 = \square$$

  A twenty-three dollars

  B two dollars, thirty cents

  C thirty-three cents

  D twenty-three cents

8. Frank's cow gives about 900 gallons of milk in a year. She gives about the same number of gallons of milk each week. About how many gallons of milk does the cow give in a week?

  A about 75

  B about 18

  C about 17

  D about 16

Read the questions. Use the strategies to choose
the answer choice that makes the most sense.

STRATEGIES

1. **A basketball arena seats 9856
   people. There are 32 seating
   sections in the arena. Each
   has the same number of seats.
   How many seats are in each
   section?**

   A 38

   B 300 R8

   C 308

   D 380

To find how many seats in a section, *divide*.

• Estimate to place each
  digit in the quotient.

• Divide the hundreds.

> **Think**
> $9856 \div 32 = \square$
> $9 \div 3 = 3$
> Try: 3

$$\begin{array}{r} 3 \\ 32\overline{)9856} \\ -96 \\ \hline 02 \end{array}$$ ← **hundreds**

• Divide the tens.

$$\begin{array}{r} 30 \\ 32\overline{)9856} \\ -96\downarrow \\ \hline 25 \end{array}$$ ← **tens**

• Divide the ones.

$$\begin{array}{r} 308 \\ 32\overline{)9856} \\ -96\downarrow \\ \hline 25\downarrow \\ 256 \\ -256 \\ \hline 0 \end{array}$$ ← **ones**

> Remember:
> **Division Steps**
> • Estimate.
> • Divide.
> • Multiply.
> • Subtract.
> • Compare.
> • Bring Down.
> • Repeat the
>   steps as
>   necessary.
> • Check.

• Check.

$$\begin{array}{r} 308 \\ \times\ 32 \\ \hline 616 \\ 9240 \\ \hline 9856 \end{array}$$ ← **dividend**

Answer choice C is correct.

Circle the letter of the correct answer choice.

2. A football stadium seats 62,304 people. There are 88 seating sections in the stadium. Each has the same number of seats. How many seats are in each section?

   A 78

   B 708

   C 780

   D 5,482,752

3. Find the quotient.

   $$81 \overline{)64{,}947}$$

   A 80

   B 81

   C 801 R66

   D 801

4. What is the most reasonable estimate of 5985 ÷ 27?

   A about 200

   B about 20

   C about 3

   D about 2

5. The quotient is 107 and the dividend is 2247. What is the divisor?

   A 21

   B 201

   C 210

   D 240,429

6. Find the quotient.

   $$9655 \div 47 = \square$$

   A 20 R20

   B 200 R 2

   C 205 R20

   D 2005 R20

7. The soccer league collected 9568 cans to buy new equipment. Each of the 46 players collected the same number. How many cans did each player collect?

   A 20

   B 28

   C 208

   D 308

Read the questions. Use the strategies to choose the answer choice that makes the most sense.

1. Look at the model.

Which names the part that is shaded?

A four   **C** 0.4

B $4\frac{1}{10}$ **D** $\frac{4}{100}$

- The model has **10** equal parts. Each part is one tenth.
- *4 tenths* or $\frac{4}{10}$ are shaded.

Remember: A fraction or a decimal can name parts of a whole.

ones.	tenths
0.	4

$\frac{4}{10} = 0.4$

Answer choice C is correct.

2. Who rode the greatest distance?

Bike Rides	
Name	**Distance**
Carlos	8.17 km
Kai	7.31 km
Eddie	8.24 km
Maggie	1.99 km

A Carlos   **C** Eddie

B Kai   **D** Maggie

- You can draw a place-value chart to help you align the digits.

ones	tenths	hundredths
8.	1	7
7.	3	1
8.	2	4
1.	9	9

First, compare the value of the digits in the greatest place.

8 ones > 7 ones > 1 ones

Think
7.31 and 1.99 cannot be correct answers.

- Compare 8.17 and 8.24: 8 = 8
- Compare digits in the tenths place. 2 > 1 So 8.24 > 8.17

Answer choice C is correct.

3. Order from least to greatest: 2.5, 2.05, 2.55, 2.46

A 2.5, 2.05, 2.46, 2.55

B 2.05, 2.46, 2.5, 2.55

C 2.55, 2.5, 2.46, 2.05

D 2.5, 2.55, 2.05, 2.46

- Draw a number line to help you order the decimals.

Think
The decimals are between 2 and 3. The decimal 2.5 is halfway between 2 and 3.

2.05   2.46 2.55

0   2.5   3

Answer choice B is correct.

Circle the letter of the correct answer choice.

4. Which of the following has the greatest value?

   A 4.05

   B 12.07

   C 12.4

   D 0.99

5. The table shows the finishing times for a 50-meter race.

Runner	Finishing Time
Meg O'Hara	7.8 sec
Victor Wong	6.92 sec
Naoki Yakamura	7.44 sec
Dave Costa	8.05 sec

Which shows the finishing times ordered from slowest to fastest?

   A 6.92, 7.44, 7.8, 8.05

   B 8.05, 7.8, 7.44, 6.92

   C 8.05, 7.44, 7.8, 6.92

   D 6.92, 7.8, 7.44, 8.05

6. Which shows the numbers in order from greatest to least?

   A 14.4, 1.44, 4.41, 4.14

   B 14.4, 4.41, 4.14, 1.44

   C 4.41, 4.14, 1.44, 14.4

   D 1.44, 4.14, 4.41, 14.4

7. Which of the following is true?

   A $0.9 < 0.09$

   B $0.99 = 9.9$

   C $0.9 > 0.09$

   D $0.09 > 0.99$

8. Eric has $80.57. Belinda has $80.75. Jerome has $87.75. Norma has $57.80. Who has the most money?

   A Eric

   B Belinda

   C Jerome

   D Norma

9. Lisa walked for two and seven tenths miles. Which point on the number line shows that decimal?

   A Q

   B R

   C S

   D T

10. Which fraction is equal to 0.8?

   A $\frac{1}{8}$ **C** $\frac{0.8}{10}$

   B $\frac{0}{8}$ **D** $\frac{8}{10}$

Read the questions. Use the strategies to choose the answer choice that makes the most sense.

STRATEGIES

1. Estimate the sum by rounding.

$$6.6$$
$$5.47$$
$$+\ 7.68$$

A about 12   C about 20

B about 17   D about 30

·Think
You can round decimals the same way you round whole numbers.

• Round the decimals to the nearest whole number.

$$6.6 \rightarrow \text{about } 7$$
$$5.47 \rightarrow \text{about } 5$$
$$+\ 7.68 \rightarrow \text{about } 8$$

• Add the rounded numbers.
$$7 + 5 + 8 = \text{about } 20$$

Answer choice C is correct.

2. Find the sum.

$$39.38 + 8.73 + 0.49$$

A 37.50

B 47.60

C 48.5

D 48.6

• Write the addition in vertical form.
• Line up the decimal points.
• Add the same way as you add whole numbers.
• Write the decimal point in the sum.

$$
\begin{array}{cccc}
1 & 1 & 2 & \\
3 & 9. & 3 & 8 \\
 & 8. & 7 & 3 \\
+ & 0. & 4 & 9 \\
\hline
4 & 8. & 6 & 0 \\
\end{array}
$$

Answer choice D is correct.

3. What is the difference between five and four tenths and two and eight tenths?

A 26

B 34

C 8.2

D 2.6

• Write the word names as decimals, and write a subtraction sentence.
$$5.4 - 2.8 = \square$$

• Write the subtraction in vertical form.

Line up the decimal points. Regroup.

Subtract tenths.

Subtract ones.

$$
\begin{array}{r}
4\ 14 \\
5.\,4 \\
-\ 2.8 \\
\end{array}
\quad
\begin{array}{r}
4\ 14 \\
5.4 \\
-\ 2.8 \\
\hline
6 \\
\end{array}
\quad
\begin{array}{r}
4\ 14 \\
5.4 \\
-\ 2.8 \\
\hline
2.6 \\
\end{array}
$$

• Write the decimal point in the difference.

Answer choice D is correct.

Circle the letter of the correct answer choice.

4. Ron lives 4.74 kilometers due north of the park. Hank lives 2.89 kilometers due south of the park. How far apart do Ron and Hank live?

   A 7.63 km

   B 6.53 km

   C 2.94 km

   D 1.85 km

5. Estimate the sum by rounding.

       40.5 + 45.24

   A about 80

   B about 85.7

   C about 86

   D about 90

6. Meg's string of beads is 40.5 inches long. Kendra's string is 9.75 inches long. About how much longer than Kendra's string of beads is Meg's string?

   A about 21 in.

   B about 30 in.

   C about 31 in.

   D about 51 in.

7. Which of the following is true?

   A $2.9 + 0.09 = 3.8$

   B $5.92 - 0.5 = 5.87$

   C $0.6 + 4.06 = 4.66$

   D $28.6 - 14.77 = 24.17$

8. Find the sum.

       17.12 + 84.36

   A 10.48

   B 67.24

   C 101.48

   D 201.48

9. What is the difference between two and sixty-four hundredths and eight tenths?

   A 0.84

   B 1.84

   C 2.56

   D 3.44

10. Find the sum.

       34.66 + 58.12 + 66.3

   A 99.41

   B 159.08

   C 159.18

   D 159.8

Read the questions. Use the strategies to choose
the answer choice that makes the most sense.

STRATEGIES

1. Find the quotient.

$$25\overline{)\$37}$$

A $.48

B $1.40

C $1.48

D $2.48

To divide with money, you can follow these steps:

• Write a decimal point and two zeros in the dividend.

• Divide as usual.

• Write the dollar sign and decimal point in the quotient.

$$
\begin{array}{r}
\$\ 1.48 \\
25\overline{)\$37.00} \\
-25 \\
\hline
120 \\
-100 \\
\hline
200 \\
-200 \\
\hline
0
\end{array}
$$

Answer choice C is correct.

2. At Mel's Market, mangoes sell for $.75 each. You also can buy mangoes in boxes of 25 for $18. Which is the better buy: 1 for $.75 or 25 for $18?

A box of 25 mangoes for $18

B box of 25 mangoes for $25

C one mango for $.75

D Both 1 for $.75 and 25 for $18 are the same price per mango.

Think

The *better buy* is the lower price per mango. To find the better buy, divide $18 by 25. Then compare the quotient with $.75, the price for a single mango.

To divide $18 ÷ 25:

• Write a decimal point and two zeros in the dividend.

$$25\overline{)\$18.00}$$

• Divide as you would with whole numbers.

$$
\begin{array}{r}
\$\ .72 \\
25\overline{)\$18.00} \\
-17\ 50 \\
\hline
50 \\
-50 \\
\hline
0
\end{array}
$$

Remember: Write the decimal point and $ in the quotient.

Mangoes are $.72 by the box.

$.72 < $.75, so the box of 25 is the better buy.

Answer choice A is correct.

Name _____

Circle the letter of the correct answer choice.

3. Twenty honeydew melons sell for $14. What is the price of one honeydew melon?

   A $.07

   B $.28

   C $.70

   D $7

4. Which is the best buy?

> 12 pens for $6
>
> 10 pens for $4
>
> 15 pens for $9

   A The prices are the same.

   B 10 pens for $4

   C 12 pens for $6

   D 15 pens for $9

5. Which of the following is true?

   A $9 \div 2 = $45

   B $60 \div 15 = $.40

   C $21 \div 25 = $.84

   D $54 \div 8 = $.675

6. What is the quotient of $16 \div 50$?

   A $.032

   B $.32

   C $3.20

   D $32

7. Six boxes of dishwasher detergent sell for $27 at Sam's Superette. Eight boxes of the same detergent sell for $34 at Graham's Grocery. One box sells for $4.35 at Mary's Market. Which store has the best buy?

   A They are the same.

   B Sam's Superette

   C Graham's Grocery

   D Mary's Market

8. Find the quotient.

$$68\overline{)\$17}$$

   A $.25

   B $.50

   C $1.25

   D $3.25

Read the questions. Use the strategies to choose the answer choice that makes the most sense.

STRATEGIES

1. A piano teacher charges $25 for a half-hour lesson. How much does she charge for 6 half-hour lessons?

   A $4.25

   B $31

   C $150

   D $1500

Think
You can write an **equation** to help you solve the problem.

- Think about what you know:
  The teacher charges $25 per lesson.
  The teacher gives 6 lessons.

- Think about what you need to know:
  How much the teacher will charge for 6 lessons

- Let the variable n stand for how much the teacher will charge for 6 lessons.

Think
You can multiply to find the total of 6 groups at $25 for each group.

- Write the equation. $25 \times 6 = n$
- Solve for n. $n = \$150$

Answer choice C is correct.

2. What number does y stand for?

   $$7 \times 3 = y \div 2$$

   A 42

   B 23

   C 21

   D 10.5

Think
- $7 \times 3 = y \div 2$ is an equation.
- The product of **7 $\times$ 3** *equals* the quotient of $y \div 2$.

To find the number that y stands for:

- Compute where possible.   **Think**
  $$7 \times 3 = 21$$ y is the missing dividend.
  $$21 = y \div 2$$

- Solve for the missing dividend.
  $$21 \times \mathbf{2} = y$$
  $$42 = y$$

Check. $7 \times 3 = 42 \div 2$
                        $\downarrow$ $\downarrow$
                        21   21

Answer choice A is correct.

Name _____

Circle the letter of the correct answer choice.

3. Anna goes to a voice teacher who charges $35 for a 45-minute lesson. How much will Anna pay for 5 lessons?

 A $40

 B $165

 C $175

 D $225

4. What number does *b* stand for?

$$7 - 5 = b$$

 A 2

 B 12

 C 35

 D 75

5. What number does *x* stand for?

$$x + x = 30$$

 A 30

 B 28

 C 15

 D 10

6. Which number is represented by *y*?

$$y + 57 = 86 - 29$$

 A 0

 B 57

 C 59

 D 114

7. There were 42,484 visitors to the zoo in July and 34,389 in August. How many more were there in July than in August?

Which equation could you use to solve this problem?

 A $42,484 \times 34,389 = n$

 B $42,484 - n = 34,389$

 C $42,484 + 34,389 = n$

 D $42,484 - 34,389 = n$

8. Find the value of the variable.

$$n \div 6 = 8$$

 A 12

 B 48

 C 54

 D 64

Read the questions. Use the strategies to choose the answer choice that makes the most sense.

1. What is the rule for this function table?

Rule: □	
Input	**Output**
20	5
36	9
52	13
64	16

A $+4$ **C** $\div 4$

B -4 **D** $\times 4$

- Number pairs in a function table go together the same way each time.
- How do the first pair go together?

Input 20	Output 5
$20 \div 4 = 5$	$20 - 15 = 5$

- Try the next number pair.

$36 \div 4 = 9$ $36 - 15 = 21$

So, "-15" is not the rule. The rule is "$\div 4$."

Test the rule with the other number pairs.

Answer choice C is correct.

2. Graph the rule of this function table. Use the graph and the rule to name the next two points that will be on the graph.

Rule: $y = 2x$				
Input	x	0	1	2	3
Output	y	0	2	4	6

A (4, 5), (5, 6)

B (4, 8), (8, 9)

C (4, 8), (5, 10)

D (4, 8), (5, 9)

- You can write the rule of the function table as the equation $y = 2x$.
- To graph the equation, write each value of x and y as an ordered pair.

(0, 0) (1, 2) (2, 4) (3, 6)

- Graph the ordered pairs.

Think
The graph is a straight line. Each point on the graph is 1 more over and 2 more up than the point before it.

- The next two points on the graph will be at (4, 8) and (5, 10).

Answer choice C is correct.

Name _____

Circle the letter of the correct answer choice.

3. Which function table shows the rule − 6 ?

A

Input	Output
50	56
35	41
25	31
6	12

B

Input	Output
72	12
54	9
42	7
30	5

C

Input	Output
50	44
35	29
25	19
6	0

D

Input	Output
0	0
2	12
4	24
6	36

4. Which function table is shown by the graph below?

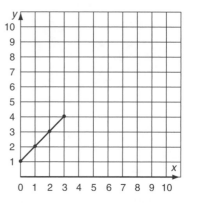

Rule: $y = x + 1$				
Input	x	0	1	2	3
Output	y	1	2	3	4

A

Rule: $y = x \div 2$				
Input	x	0	2	4	6
Output	y	0	1	2	3

B

Rule: $y = 2x$				
Input	x	0	1	2	3
Output	y	0	2	4	6

C

Rule: $y = x$				
Input	x	0	2	4	6
Output	y	0	2	4	6

D

Read the questions. Use the strategies to choose the answer choice that makes the most sense.

STRATEGIES

1. **Which symbol completes this number sentence?**

   $$48 \div 6 \ \square \ 5 + 3$$

   A $>$

   B $<$

   C $=$

   D $\neq$

Remember:
$>$ *is greater than* $<$ *is less than*
$=$ *is equal to* $\neq$ *is not equal to*

To find the correct symbol:

• Simplify the expression on each side of the missing symbol.

$$48 \div 6 \ \square \ 5 + 3$$
$$8 \quad \square \quad 8$$

• Compare. Write $>$, $<$, $=$, or $\neq$.

$$8 = 8$$

So $48 \div 6 = 5 + 3$

Answer choice C is correct.

2. **Simplify.**

   $$4 \div 2 + (3 \times 5) - 9 = n$$

   A $n = 4$

   B $n = 8$

   C $n = 15$

   D $n = 17$

If a problem has parentheses, you need to follow these rules:

• Compute inside the parentheses first.

$$4 \div 2 + (3 \times 5) - 9 = n$$
$$15$$

• Follow the order of operations. Multiply and divide in order from left to right.

$$4 \div 2 + 15 - 9 = n$$
$$2$$

• Add and subtract in order from left to right.

$$2 + 15 - 9 = n$$
$$17 - 9 = 8$$
$$n = 8$$

Answer choice B is correct.

Circle the letter of the correct answer choice.

3. Which symbol or symbols completes the number sentence?

$$6 + (12 - 5) \,\square\, 30 - (5 + 7)$$

A $=$

B $\neq$ or $<$

C $\neq$ or $>$

D $>$

4. Simplify.

$$(d \times 3) - 9 = (14 + 7) - 9$$

A $d = 4$ **C** $d = 9$

B $d = 7$ **D** $d = 21$

5. Look at the problem below.

$$\square = \blacklozenge - 6$$

If $\blacklozenge = 18$, what is $\square$?

A 3

B 6

C 12

D 24

6. Which goes in the box to make this number sentence true?

$$240 \div 8 = 20 + \square$$

A 5×2

B 5

C 12×4

D $10 \div 2$

7. The sum of $a + b$ equals 24. If $a = 18$, which equation can be used to find the value of b?

A $b - 18 = 24$

B $18 + b = 24$

C $a - b = 24$

D $a + 18 = 24$

8. What is the value of the variable?

$$(4 + 8) + 9 = 3 \times a$$

A 7

B 9

C 12

D 18

9. What number goes in the box to make this number sentence true?

$$\frac{1}{5} + \left(\frac{2}{5} + \frac{2}{5}\right) = \frac{3}{6} + \square$$

A $\frac{1}{6}$

B $\frac{3}{6}$

C $\frac{1}{5}$

D 1

Read the problem. Use the Problem-Solving Guide below to help you think about the answer choices.

Joe, Karen, Lara, and Eli competed in the 100-meter dash. Joe's time was 12.8 seconds. Karen's time was 12.74 seconds. Lara's time was 12.4 seconds, and Eli's time was 12.58 seconds. Who won the race?

A Lara   **C** Karen

B Joe   **D** Eli

PROBLEM-SOLVING GUIDE

1 Understand the Question

- The question is asking you to compare the running time of four runners.

- You need to choose the answer with the name of the fastest runner.

2 Understand Word Meanings

- In a race, the winner is the one who runs the race in the **least** time.

- The runner whose time is given as the **least** decimal is the winner.

3 Understand How to Solve

- Compare the four decimals to solve the problem.
- Align the digits by place value.

tens	ones	tenths	hundredths
1	2.	8	0
1	2.	7	4
1	2.	4	0
1	2.	5	8

Remember: Write zeros to make the same number of decimal places.

- Begin at the greatest place. The value of digits is the same in the tens and ones place, so compare the value of the decimals in the tenths place.

$$0.4 < 0.5 < 0.7 < 0.8 \longrightarrow \text{the least decimal is } 12.40$$

- Reread the problem. Who ran the race in 12.40 seconds?

4 Circle the Letter of the Correct Answer Choice.

Answer choice A is correct. Lara won the race.

Name _____

Circle the letter of the correct answer choice.

The overall size of a regulation soccer field is 100 yards long and 60 yards wide. What is the area of the field?

A 320 yd²   **C** 3200 yd²

B 600 yd²   **D** 6000 yd²

100 yd

60 yd

Complete each sentence.

1 Understand the Question

• A soccer field has the shape of a _____.

• The problem gives you the _____ and _____ of the field.

• The question asks you to find the _____ of the field.

---

2 Understand Word Meanings: regulation

• Think about the word *regulation*.
The *root word* of **regulation** is **regular**.
You know that **regular** means "normal" or "standard."

• Write what you think what a **regulation** field means. _____

---

3 Understand How to Solve

• The area of the field is the number of _____ yards that cover it.
• Use a formula to find the area of the soccer field.

$$\text{Area} = \underline{\hspace{3cm}} \times \underline{\hspace{3cm}}.$$

• Multiply _____ × _____ to find the area.

• The area of the soccer field is _____ yd².

---

4 Circle the Letter of the Correct Answer Choice.

Answer choice _____ is correct. The area of the soccer field is 6000 yd².

Name _____

Circle the letter of the correct answer choice.

1. Jerome bought a poster that is 24 inches wide and 36 inches long. He wants to put a wooden frame around its border. What is the total length of the wood he needs for his frame?

   A 5 ft   **C** 10 ft

   B 6 ft   **D** 72 ft

2. Mr. Betamit will give the same number of marker pens to each of his 40 art students. He has 166 marker pens. At most, how many can he give to each student?

   A 3

   B 4

   C 5

   D 40

3. A class of 22 students spent a total of $191.75 on books at the book fair. Each student spent about the same amount of money. About how much money did each student spend at the book fair?

   A about $5

   B about $10

   C about $50

   D about $100

4. A ferry that runs to an island can carry 44 passengers on one trip. A tour guide needs to take 302 people to the island. What is the least number of ferries needed?

   A 5   **C** 7

   B 6   **D** 8

5. A rugby field is 160 yards long and 75 yards wide. What is the area of the field?

   A 12,000 yd

   B 12,000 yd^2

   C 1200 yd^2

   D 235 yd^2

6. The sketch shows the shape of Leona's new loft. What is the area of the loft?

   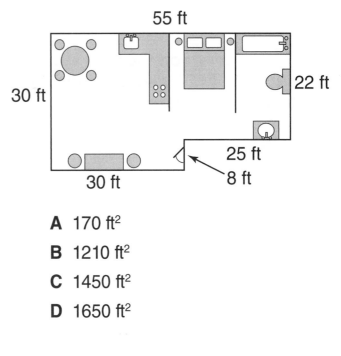

   A 170 ft^2

   B 1210 ft^2

   C 1450 ft^2

   D 1650 ft^2

7. Karen ran 10.5 km on Monday, 11.25 km on Wednesday, and 14.4 km on Friday. How much farther did she run on Friday than on Monday?

A 3.15 km

B 3.9 km

C 24.9 km

D 25.65 km

8. In four gymnastics events, Liam had scores of 5.45, 5.6, 4.95, and 5.05. Which shows his scores in order from highest to lowest?

A 4.95, 5.05, 5.45, 5.6

B 4.95, 5.45, 5.05, 5.6

C 5.6, 5.45, 5.05, 4.95

D 5.6, 4.95, 5.45, 5.05

9. Sam's team won the boat race in a time of 44.85 minutes. What is that number rounded to the nearest minute?

A 45 min

B 44.9 min

C 44.8 min

D 44 min

10. The Frozen Niagara Tour of Mammoth Cave National Park is 0.75 miles long. The Grand Avenue Tour is 4 miles long. What is the combined length of the two tours?

A 2.25 mi

B 3.25 mi

C 3.5 mi

D 4.75 mi

11. Gil made the following function table to show how the number of books he reads compares with the number that Luis reads.

Luis	Gil
1	3
4	12
8	24
10	☐

How many books would Gil read in the time it would take Luis to read 10 books?

A 30

B 26

C 22

D 12

Circle the letter of the correct answer choice.

12. **A shoebox is 30 centimeters long, 12 centimeters wide, and 8 centimeters high. What is the volume of the shoebox?**

   A 50 cubic centimeters

   B 288 cubic centimeters

   C 2880 cubic centimeters

   D 28,800 cubic centimeters

13. **Alberto drew the following net. It folds to form a solid figure. What is the figure that the net will form?**

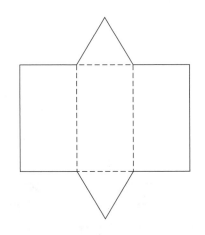

   A a rectangular prism

   B a triangular prism

   C a cube

   D a square pyramid

14. **Wendy made the following graph for the equation $y = x - 2$?**

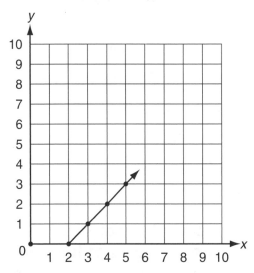

Which ordered pair names a point that lies on Wendy's graph?

   A (8, 6)

   B (6, 8)

   C (7, 10)

   D (6, 12)

15. **A park is in the shape of a square. Each side is 8 kilometers in length. What is the perimeter of the park?**

   A 16 km

   B 32 km

   C 64 km

   D 80 km

16. Ken will give an equal number of pens to each of 12 students. He has 188 pens. At most, how many pens can he give to each student? How many pens will he have left?

A 16 pens; 0 pens left over

B 15 pens; 8 pens left over

C 15 pens; 12 pens left over

D 14 pens; 20 pens left over

17. Kate needs 2 super-sandwiches for every 8 guests at her party. How many super-sandwiches does she need if she has 24 party guests?

A 6

B 12

C 16

D 48

18. Rafael picked 265 strawberries. He will pack them into small boxes that hold 30 berries each. What is the greatest number of boxes Rafael can fill?

A 9

B 8

C 7

D 6

19. Gerry hiked for four and three tenths miles. Which decimal shows how far he hiked?

A 0.43

B 4.03

C 4.3

D 43.10

20. Four friends went to a ballgame. Tony brought $12.50 with him for snacks. Jin brought $20. Leah brought $15.50. Tracy brought $15.05. Who brought the least amount of money to the ballgame?

A Leah

B Tracy

C Jin

D Tony

21. The train goes from Brooks to Dale. It passes through Grove on the way. It is 14.8 miles from Brooks to Grove. It is 32 miles from Dale to Brooks. How far is it from Grove to Dale?

A 17.2 mi

B 18.2 mi

C 18.6 mi

D 46.8 mi

Name _____

Circle the letter of the correct answer choice.

1. **If you fold each of these patterns along the dashed lines, you will form a solid figure. Which figure will have a volume of 64 cubic centimeters?**

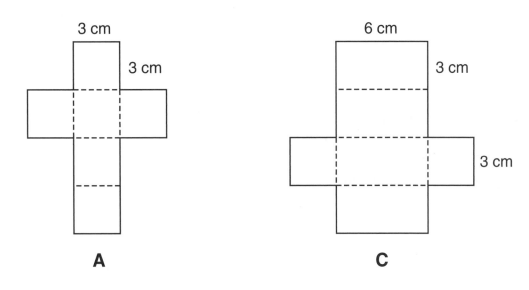

3 cm · 3 cm

A

6 cm · 3 cm · 3 cm

C

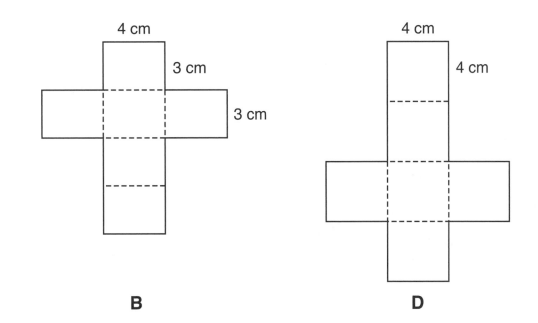

4 cm · 3 cm · 3 cm

B

4 cm · 4 cm

D

2. Which equation shows how to place parentheses in order to make the equation below true?

$$4 + 3 \times 5 - 2 = 33$$

A $4 + (3 \times 5) - 2 = 33$

B $(4 + 3 \times 5) - 2 = 33$

C $(4 + 3) \times 5 - 2 = 33$

D $4 + 3 \times (5 - 2) = 33$

3. You draw line segments to connect each set of ordered pairs on the coordinate grid below. Which set of ordered pairs will form a right isosceles triangle?

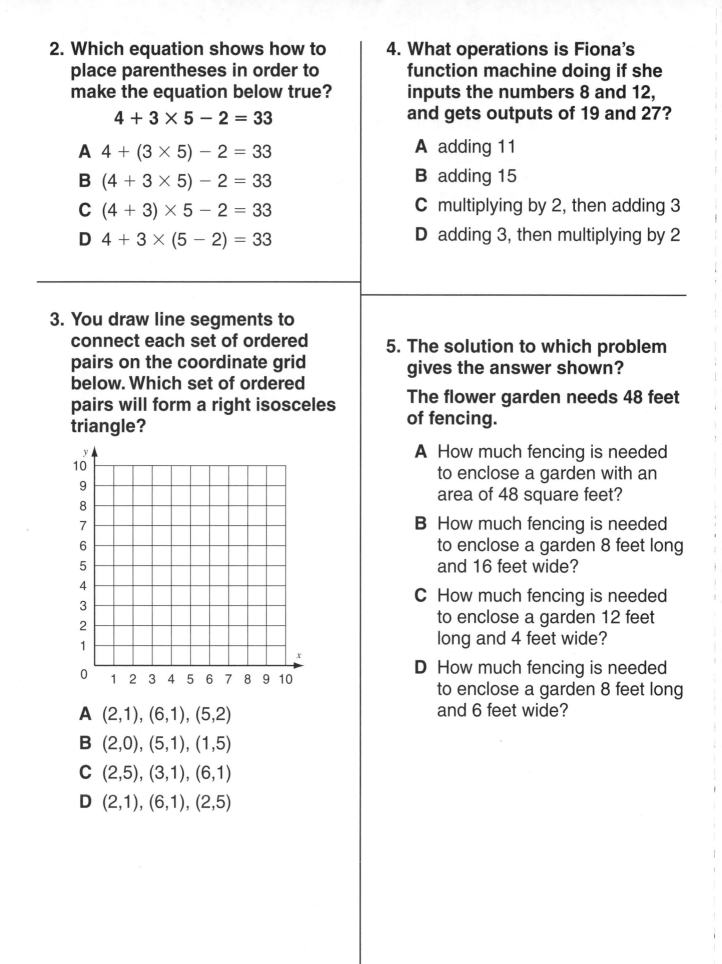

A (2,1), (6,1), (5,2)

B (2,0), (5,1), (1,5)

C (2,5), (3,1), (6,1)

D (2,1), (6,1), (2,5)

4. What operations is Fiona's function machine doing if she inputs the numbers 8 and 12, and gets outputs of 19 and 27?

A adding 11

B adding 15

C multiplying by 2, then adding 3

D adding 3, then multiplying by 2

5. The solution to which problem gives the answer shown?

The flower garden needs 48 feet of fencing.

A How much fencing is needed to enclose a garden with an area of 48 square feet?

B How much fencing is needed to enclose a garden 8 feet long and 16 feet wide?

C How much fencing is needed to enclose a garden 12 feet long and 4 feet wide?

D How much fencing is needed to enclose a garden 8 feet long and 6 feet wide?

6. Which expression gives the number of minutes in two weeks?

    A 60×14

    B $60 \times 24 \times 7$

    C $60 \times 24 \times 14$

    D $60 \times 60 \times 24 \times 14$

7. Which two numbers have a sum of 2.25?

    A 1.5 and $\frac{1}{4}$

    B $1\frac{3}{4}$ and 0.5

    C 2.8 and 0.55

    D $\frac{3}{4}$ and $1\frac{3}{4}$

8. I am a 4-digit number. The sum of my digits is 15. My hundredths digit is twice what my tens digit is. My ones digit is twice what my tenths digit is. What number am I?

    A 81.24

    B 22.16

    C 42.18

    D 421.8

9. The school playground is a square measuring 40 meters on a side. The sides of the new school playground will be twice as long as they are now. What will be the area of the new playground?

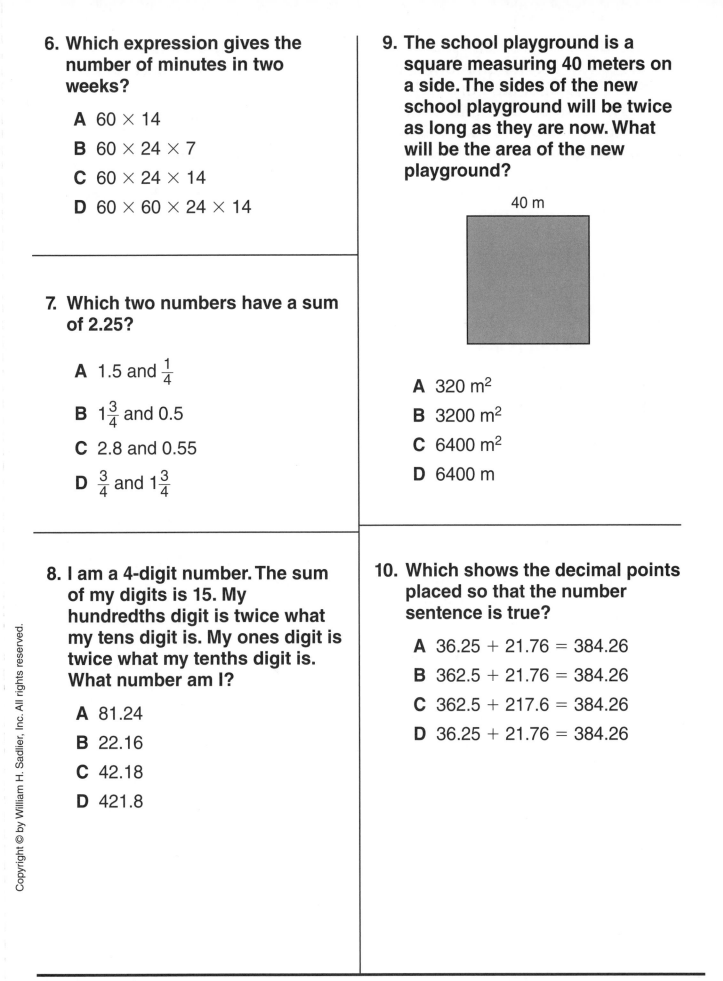

40 m

    A 320 m²

    B 3200 m²

    C 6400 m²

    D 6400 m

10. Which shows the decimal points placed so that the number sentence is true?

    A $36.25 + 21.76 = 384.26$

    B $362.5 + 21.76 = 384.26$

    C $362.5 + 217.6 = 384.26$

    D $36.25 + 21.76 = 384.26$

Use following Chapter 14.

11. In a division problem, the divisor is 24. The quotient is a 2-digit number also divisible by 8. The sum of the digits of the 3-digit dividend is 15. What is the quotient?

A 40

B 48

C 96

D 960

12. For every mile that Juan walks in a walkathon, Liz says she will walk 3 miles. If Juan were to walk n miles, how far would Liz have to walk?

A n mi

B $3 \times n$ mi

C $3 + n$ mi

D $3 - n$ mi

13. Which two decimals in the box have a sum of 12.53 and a difference of 1.53?

7.03	2.03	3.10	5.5	2.84

A 2.03 and 5.5

B 3.10 and 2.84

C 7.03 and 5.5

D 2.03 and 7.03

14. What is the distance from Highmount to Green Valley?

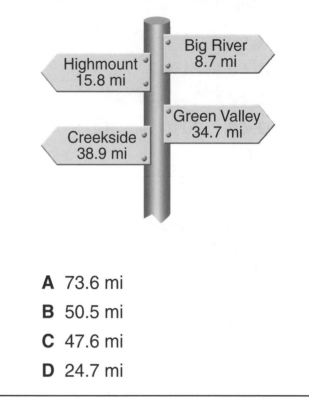

A 73.6 mi

B 50.5 mi

C 47.6 mi

D 24.7 mi

15. The figure below is made up of large and small squares. How many squares are there in all? How many right angles are there in all?

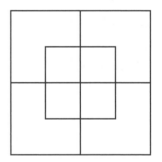

A 8 squares, 32 right angles

B 10 squares, 36 right angles

C 10 squares, 40 right angles

D 9 squares, 36 right angles

Use following Chapter 14.

Name _____

Circle the letter of the correct answer choice.

1. **The Sawtooth National Recreation Area has 729,332 acres. Which shows this rounded to the nearest ten thousand?**

   A 700,000   **C** 730,000

   B 729,000   **D** 800,000

2. **Which is the least common multiple (LCM) of 9 and 12?**

   A 3   **C** 24

   B 9   **D** 36

3. **Ashley has 1 twenty-dollar bill. She spends $4.55 for lunch and $11.79 for a hat. Which shows how much money she has left?**

   A $1.00

   B $3.66

   C $7.24

   D $7.44

4. **Hunter buys 5 boxes of greeting cards. Each box costs $5.97. What is the total cost?**

   A $28.85

   B $29.75

   C $29.85

   D $29.95

5. **Which fraction is in simplest form?**

   A $\frac{3}{6}$ **C** $\frac{6}{10}$

   B $\frac{3}{8}$ **D** $\frac{8}{14}$

6. **What is the dividend?**

   $$4\overline{)\,74}$$

   A 70   **C** 286

   B 78   **D** 296

7. **Look at the figures below.**

   Which statement is true?

   A They both have the same area.

   B They both have the same perimeter.

   C They both have the same length.

   D They both have the same width.

8. A solid figure has 5 faces, 8 edges, and 5 vertices. Which figure is it?

    A square pyramid

    B rectangular prism

    C triangular prism

    D sphere

9. Abby makes hats for a party. Of the hats, $\frac{1}{3}$ are red, $\frac{1}{3}$ are blue, and the rest are green. What fraction of the hats are red or blue?

    A $\frac{2}{6}$ **C** $\frac{3}{3}$

    B $\frac{2}{3}$ **D** 2

10. Find the quotient.

$$476 \div 91 = \square$$

    A 43,316

    B 567

    C 5 R21

    D 4 R112

11. What number does n stand for?

$$n + n = 12$$

    A 24

    B 12

    C 8

    D 6

12. Bay Newsstand receives 85 magazines. The magazines are in bundles of 24. How many bundles are there? How many loose magazines are there?

    A 3 bundles; 15 loose magazines

    B 3 bundles; 13 loose magazines

    C 4 bundles

    D 24 bundles; 61 loose magazines

Use the table below to answer questions 13 and 14.

400-Meter Race	
Runner	**Time**
Lee	49.3 s
Andy	47.9 s
Rick	51.06 s
Jim	47.95 s

13. Four runners ran a 400-meter race. Who finished the race third?

    A Lee   **C** Rick

    B Andy   **D** Jim

14. What is the difference between the fastest and slowest times?

    A 1.76 s

    B 3.16 s

    C 4 s

    D 4.16 s

Name _____

Circle the letter of the correct answer choice.

15. Find the sum.

$$10.37 + 24.4$$

A 35.77　　　**C** 34.41

B 34.77　　　**D** 34

16. A bag of 12 peaches sells for $3.60. You can also buy one peach for $.30. Which is the better buy?

A bag of 12 peaches for $3.60

B bag of 12 peaches for $12.00

C 1 peach for $.30

D The prices are the same.

17. What is the value of y?

$$7 + y = 18$$

A 25　　　**C** 11

B 19　　　**D** 1

18. Which of the following best describes the figure below?

$$\longleftrightarrow$$
$$\longleftrightarrow$$

A parallel lines

B perpendicular lines

C intersecting lines

D angle

19. What is the probability of the spinner landing on green?

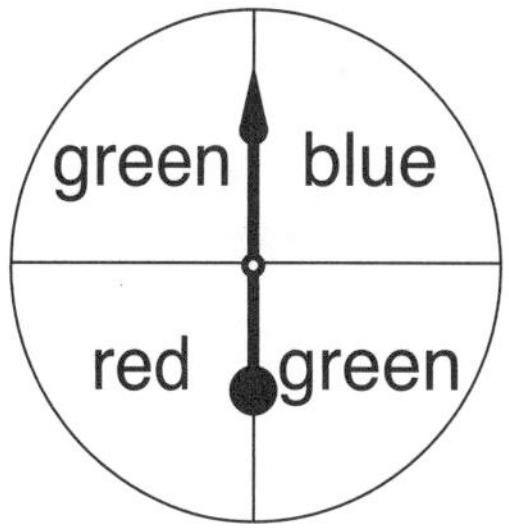

A $\frac{2}{2}$　　　**C** $\frac{1}{4}$

B $\frac{1}{3}$　　　**D** $\frac{2}{4}$

20. Michael walks every day. He starts at 11:45 A.M. He walks for 40 minutes. What time does Michael's walk end?

A 12:25 A.M.

B 12:25 P.M.

C 11:05 A.M.

D 1:05 P.M.

21. Mel ran $\frac{5}{8}$ mile in the morning and $\frac{3}{4}$ mile in the afternoon. What is the total distance that Mel ran?

A $1\frac{3}{8}$ mile　　　**C** $1\frac{1}{4}$ mile

B $1\frac{1}{8}$ mile　　　**D** $\frac{1}{8}$ mile

Use the table below to answer questions 22 and 23.

Al surveyed students in his school to find their favorite activities. Each student chose one activity. The bar graph shows the results.

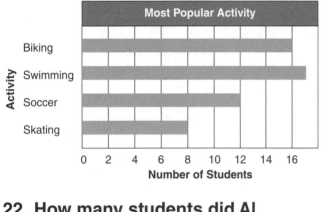

22. How many students did Al survey?

   A 53   **C** 26

   B 52   **D** 17

23. How many more students chose biking than soccer?

   A 16   **C** 4

   B 12   **D** 2

24. What is the rule for this function table?

Rule: ?					
Input	x	1	2	3	4	5
Output	y	4	8	12	16	20

   A $y = 4x$ **C** $y = 4 + x$

   B $y = x$ **D** $x = 4y$

25 Which polygon has 6 angles?

   A pentagon

   B an octagon

   C a hexagon

   D a quadrilateral

26. A pilot flew 23,056 miles in 44 hours. How many miles per hour did the pilot travel?

   A 501   **C** 5240

   B 524   **D** 1,014,464

27. Use the order of operations to simplify.

$$\left(\frac{1}{8} + \frac{7}{8}\right) \times \left(\frac{1}{4} + \frac{6}{8}\right)$$

   A 1   **C** $1\frac{1}{2}$

   B $1\frac{1}{4}$ **D** 2

28. Ted cut $\frac{1}{4}$ yard from a board $\frac{3}{4}$ yard long. How long is the board now?

   A 2 yards

   B 1 yard

   C $\frac{2}{8}$ yard

   D $\frac{1}{2}$ yard